# VEGAN
# HEALTH
# PLAN

# THE VEGAN HEALTH PLAN

A PRACTICAL GUIDE
TO HEALTHY LIVING

## Amanda Sweet

*Arlington Books*
London

THE VEGAN HEALTH PLAN
*first published in 1987 by*
*Arlington Books (Publishers) Ltd*
*15–17 King Street, St James's*
*London SW1*

*Reprinted 1988, 1990*

*British Library Cataloguing-in-Publication Data*
*Sweet, Amanda*
*The vegan health plan*
*1. Vegetarian cookery*
*I. Title*
*641.5'636        TX837*

*ISBN 0–85140–699–8*

*Typeset by Inforum Ltd, Portsmouth*
*Printed and bound in Great Britain by*
*Billing & Sons Ltd, Worcester*

# Contents

## 5 Flavouring Vegan Foods

## 6 Recipes

## Acknowledgements

I would like to express my most sincere thanks to my mother, Ann Sweet, for her time and patience in typing the original draft of the book and also to Fiona Cownie, Celia Caspell and Fred Lancaster for all their invaluable help and advice; John Harland for his excellent illustrations and Stephen for his financial and moral support whilst I was writing the book.

This book is dedicated to everyone,
everywhere, who wanted me to write it.

# 1

# WHY VEGANISM?

## Vegans and Health

*Veganism may be defined as a way of living which seeks to exclude, as far as possible and practical, all forms of exploitation of, and cruelty to, the animal kingdom for food, clothing or any other purpose. In dietary terms it refers to the practice of dispensing with all animal produce — including flesh, fish, fowl, eggs, (non-human) animal milks, and their derivatives, with the taking of honey being left to individual conscience.*

The Vegan
Winter 1985

Good health is a state of mental and physical well-being that enables us to accomplish our aims and enjoy life to the full. Health is created through the exercise we take, sleep, fresh air, our attitude to life, and largely, by what we eat.

Studies carried out on vegan and omnivorous (vegetable and animal matter eating) volunteers show that a well balanced vegan diet, that is, a diet low in saturated fat, cholesterol and sugar but high in polyunsaturated fat and fibre, can be a major factor in the prevention of many common degenerative diseases.

### Avoiding disease

*Heart disease* may be characterised by a build up in the arteries of a fatty protein material containing cholesterol. Cholesterol is produced in the body by the liver and is also found in animal foods such as cheese, eggs, milk, meat and saturated fats e.g., suet, lard and butter. Consuming foods which contain cholesterol does not automatically increase the level of cholesterol in the blood. The liver acts as a cholesterol regulator, producing less when cholesterol intake is high. However, the consumption of saturated fat overrides this effect leading to high blood cholesterol. The consumption of polyunsaturated fats — found in vegetable oils, nuts and seeds — actually lowers blood cholesterol levels. (see p. 26).

Tests have shown vegans to have much lower blood cholesterol levels than omnivores and are therefore less likely to suffer from various forms of heart disease; in fact some patients suffering from heart conditions have been advised to follow a vegan diet.

Meat eating peoples such as the Masai and the Eskimos have extremely high incidences of degenerative disease — a marked contrast to vegetarian tribes such as the Hunzakuts of Kashmir or the members of 'The Farm' (a vegan community in Tennessee) where such diseases are unknown.

*Breast cancer* has also been linked to a high fat diet — women suffering from it have been shown to have very high blood lipid (fat) levels. Women on meat diets are also thought to produce higher levels of certain hormones associated with cancer, which may also be a contributing factor. Vegan women generally have much lower blood lipid levels; consequently they rarely contract breast cancer. (Vegan women also tend to suffer less from premenstrual water-retention and have decreased blood loss and less pain with their monthly period than omnivorous women.)

Vegans consume at least twice as much dietary fibre as omnivores and this has three very important health benefits. (i) As the fibre in vegan food is so bulky the diet is self-regulating and there is less tendency to overeat thus reducing the risk of *obesity*, *gallstones* and *high blood-pressure*. Fibre absorbs water and swells up so food gets pushed through the digestive system more quickly and efficiently; whereas in low fibre diets, some food is never eliminated and turns to body fat, particularly *cellulite* on the thighs and buttocks — something vegans rarely suffer from. (ii) Vegan foods, for example pulses and grains, are composed of complex carbohydrates which take longer to break down into sugar in the body than simple carbohydrates, such as white sugar, helping to keep blood sugar levels constant and reducing the risk of *diabetes, high blood pressure* and *obesity*.

(iii) The vegan diet, high in fibre and low in saturated fat and sugar, may contribute to the prevention of certain *cancers*, notably that of the bowel. The longer transit times of food from mouth to anus in low fibre diets allows toxins produced by bacteria in the gut to remain longer in the intestines. This may result in *bowel cancer*, *diverticular disease*, *constipation*, *appendicitis* and related disorders such as *haemorrhoids*, *varicose veins* and *gallstones*.

Fibre also binds itself to cholesterol and carries it out of the body thereby helping to reduce the risks of heart disease.

*Other disorders linked to milk, cheese and meat*: Diets which are high in dairy produce may overload the liver and kidneys with protein, contributing to disease of these organs. Excessive protein can also make you *overweight*, *temperamental* and *overstressed*.

In addition, milk protein produces excess mucus in the body which leads to *colds*, *catarrh* and *sinus problems*. It also causes allergies that lead to *asthma*, *eczema* and *migraine*. Some adults do not possess the enzymes necessary to break down milk sugar which then builds up in the intestines resulting in *diarrhoea* or *cramps*. Soya milk, the vegan 'dairy' food does not cause any such allergies.

Meat is an acid-forming food which requires twice as much hydrochloric acid in the stomach to break it down than vegetables which are alkali-forming. As excessive acidity in the stomach can lead to *ulcers*, it follows that vegans are less prone to them.

Vegans also rarely suffer from *gout* caused by an excess of sodium urate crystals in the skin or joints. These crystals are formed from substances called 'purines' which are found predominantly in beef, fish, offal and pork.

There is much evidence to suggest that vegans tend to have more stamina and prolonged youthfulness than omnivores. This is possibly due to the abundance of minerals and vitamins (particularly B-complex) found in their diet which help to keep their bodies healthy, their minds alert, and their skin soft and supple.


**Economy**

The idea held by some omnivores (and often used as an argument for not changing the diet) that vegan food is expensive and not easily obtainable, is totally unfounded.

Meat is by far the most expensive item on the shopping list, followed by dairy foods and eggs. If one compares the price of vegan protein foods such as pulses, grains and tofu on a weight-for-weight basis, it becomes clear that they are not only considerably cheaper but will go further when cooking for a family.

For example, 8 oz (225 g) of lentils or beans made into a savoury dish will serve four people whereas an 8 oz (225 g) steak or a chop would only serve one person. Meat shrinks when it cooks — pulses expand!

Vegan foods such as pulses and grains have a very long shelf-life so they can be purchased in bulk which is cheaper and saves on shopping trips. This is also a help to single people who cook for themselves and may only want small quantities of something — they can just reseal the bag and keep the food until required again, something that is not very easily done with a piece of meat.

After the initial outlay to restock your store cupboard, the basic vegetable, fruit, pulse and grain diet occasionally supplemented with the more expensive foods will maintain good health and provide greater taste, colour, texture, interest and nutritional value at a cost far less than even the most frugal omnivorous diet.

Vegan foods are increasingly available with most good supermarkets now stocking a wide range of pulses, nuts, whole-grains, soya milks, vegetable oils, additive-free preserves, sugar-free juices, mueslis, dried fruits and frozen convenience meals at competitive prices. Some may even have an organic vegetable counter.

Wholefood or 'health food' shops usually stock a full range of dried pulses, nuts, herbs and spices, vegan margarines, tofu, soya milks, grains, dried fruits and convenience meals. They may also sell cookery books, other vegan literature and 'cruelty-free' toiletries and cosmetics.

I am sure that in the next few years we are going to see a massive increase in the range of vegan goods available with many major food manufacturers already investigating the possibilities of additive-free organic produce.

It is up to us, as consumers, to demand healthier, humane food for ourselves and our families.

## Food Contamination

Vegan food reduces the risk of contamination by antibiotic and hormone residues; pesticides, insecticides, and food poisoning organisms.

Intensive factory farming of animals is causing a large increase in the incidence of animal disease. Consequently, millions of pounds are spent every year on improving various antibiotics to combat disease and relieve stress. Experiments have shown that residues of these antibiotics are present in foods sold for consumption, especially milk and veal. Perhaps even more horrifying is the fact that some of the bacteria present in animals (particularly calves) are developing a resistance to several commonly used antibiotics, presenting an even more serious threat to the consumer.

Hormones used to promote growth, increase fertility and produce multiple births are now given routinely in feed and have two major side-effects, firstly they produce a higher fat content in the meat and secondly they leave a residue. Certain hormones still used in Britain (but banned in most other European countries) are thought to be carcinogenic, e.g. diethylstilbesterol.

The long term cumulative effects of the mixtures of additives, preservatives, colourings and flavourings that are standard components of processed foods have not yet been properly investigated. Evidence suggests that they can cause headaches, skin problems, various allergies and diarrhoea. Studies have shown that some children whose diet contains a high proportion of additives are more likely to exhibit aggression and hyperactivity. When the offending foods are removed from the diet the child's behaviour improves correspondingly.

The increased demands for meat have also led to an extensive use of pesticides and insecticides to improve the yields of crops grown for feed.

Pesticide residues are retained in animal fats (particularly in dairy products which have shown very high levels of contamination) as they are difficult to break down, and some may be passed to the consumer. Pesticide poisoning may cause headaches, fatigue, nausea, and in severe cases, convulsions.

Some fungicides, accumulations of which are highly poisonous, have been found to taint chicken flesh and eggs.

Four out of five cases of food poisoning are traced to meat and meat products. Intensively reared chicken is the biggest offender as it is the largest carrier of salmonella bacteria.

By not consuming meat, milk, cheese and eggs; avoiding processed foods; and consuming as much organically grown produce as possible, vegans can reduce the risks of possible illness due to the consumption of antibiotic, pesticide, insecticide and hormone residues, and food poisoning organisms.

## Conservation Considerations

*We should be growing food not feed, supplying need not greed.*

Ghandi
(1869–1948)

It is absolute nonsense to suggest that vegans only care about animals not humans. Vegans feel it is morally unjustifiable to feed nutritious food to animals bred for meat and milk, when it not only involves incomprehensible wastage, but also serves to intensify food shortages in the Third World.

Deforestation on a worldwide scale has taken place and large areas have gone for grazing land. This not only seriously affects the environmental balance and ecology of the planet but deprives humans of potential sources of fuel, building materials and food. Over half of the world's fertile land is used for rearing animals — if crops were to be grown instead, the returns in terms of nutrition, and conservation of resources, would be enormous.

An omnivorous diet requires over eight times as much water and over five times as much land compared with the demands of a vegan diet. It takes more water to produce meat (to grow feed and in meat processing) than it does to produce an equal weight of vegetables and crops such as cereals and pulses which produce far more protein per acre than either meat or milk.

Even if they are confined to factory farms and not grazing land, animals still have to be fed. This involves millions of tons of protein such as soya beans and barley, obtained from the bulk of our agricultural land, only a very small percentage of which is used to feed man directly. As a result, animals are supplying us indirectly and uneconomically with what we should be eating first hand. A further example of this is ground nut protein, one of the most important famine relief foods in India, which Britain imports to feed factory farm animals and chickens.

Probably the biggest irony of all is that in the West where more meat and dairy produce are consumed than anywhere else in the world, not only do we produce quantities in excess of the demand but the majority of people eat twice as much animal protein as their body actually needs.

In Britain alone, nearly half the acreage suitable for crops is used to produce cereals which, if they were not fed to animals (or added to the ever increasing EEC grain mountain) would provide every member of the population with the recommended daily allowance of protein and more than enough calories required by the body.

## Exploitation of Animals by Man

### Cattle

The dairy cow is probably one of the most exploited animals on our planet. As a mammal, she must give birth in order to lactate. Consequently she must be pregnant every year of her unnaturally short life and this is usually achieved by artificial insemination.

During pregnancy she may suffer various ailments (especially mastitis), the treatment of which requires large doses of antibiotics that may remain in her milk (see p. 13). After birth, the calf is only allowed to suckle for 3 days before being removed from its mother and destined for one of five fates depending on sex and build.

Once the calf is removed the cow is milked twice a day so that humans can get the 'bottle' we are assured every one needs.

As soon as she comes on heat she is again made pregnant to continue the milk producing cycle. After four or five years, her milk yield drops and she will be sent for immediate slaughter. This compares to a normal life expectancy of 14 years. The worn out meat is often exported as it is not popular in Britain. Much of it finds its way into the burger trade.

Female calves are removed from the mother at birth and hand-reared thereby maximising the amount of milk sold to the consumer. They are fed milk substitutes and start the cycle of continuous pregnancies at the age of 18 to 24 months.

Male calves suitable for beef may be allowed to suckle for a week. After this period many are sent to market for sale to intensive beef units where they are confined to fattening pens, deprived of exercise and overfed so they put on weight quickly prior to slaughter. If they are lucky some may be allowed to graze before going to the fattening pens. In Britain 70–80% of our beef comes from the dairy industry.

Some male calves go straight to white veal units where they spend their 14 week life shut in a crate in the dark being fed on a special diet deficient in iron (to keep the flesh fashionably white) and deprived of the roughage necessary to their digestive system. This leads to cravings for solids and as they have no bedding they often chew their crates, or each other. Many are too weak to stand when they are eventually herded to the slaughter lorry.

Any sickly or weak calves are slaughtered immediately and go to make veal and ham pies, baby food or pet food. Their stomach enzymes provide the rennet used in commercial cheese making.

Exceptionally, a male calf may be suitable to rear as a stud bull. He will be allowed to suckle for a longer period and then reared on a special diet to produce maximum fertility and good physique. From 10 to 12 months of age he will either serve cows or will be subjected to the 'electro-ejaculator' and the sperm used for artificial insemination. His life will be spent in solitary confinement until he is past his prime when he will be castrated and fattened up for beef. If his sperm has been frozen he may continue to sire calves for years after his death.

### Sheep and goats

The situation is just as grim for sheep and goats, particularly since the recent increase in demand for sheep and goats' milk yoghurt and cheese which are promoted as 'allergy-free', 'natural' or 'healthy' products.

Sheep and goats undergo carefully controlled pregnancies so that they give birth more often and at the most profitable time of year. Kids and lambs from dairy goats and sheep are removed from the mother shortly after birth and bottle-reared so that all the milk can be used to produce dairy products.

Male kids and lambs do not produce milk so they are either slaughtered when a few days old or castrated and fattened up for slaughter at 2–3 months of age. They sometimes suffer live export to the Middle East for ritual Halal (Moslem) or Kosher (Jewish) slaughter.

## Egg production

Over 90% of British egg-laying hens are confined in enormous battery farms from the age of 18 weeks. Their lives are spent in dimly lit cages, stacked in tiers, where five hens occupy a space not big enough for one to fully stretch her wings.

They stand on slanting wire mesh (which is easier to clean than straw) and may consequently develop damaged feet and claws. Food is dispensed in a trough at the front of the cage, droppings and eggs are carried away on a conveyor belt.

Hens are naturally territorial and aggressive and the frustration of being caged often leads to cannibalism and feather pecking. Many farmers routinely cut the beaks off their birds to prevent this happening.

One year-old hens usually suffer a forced moult to speed them over their natural rest from laying. The following year when their laying days are coming to an end, they are slaughtered. Worn out battery chicken meat is used for pet food, baby food, pâtés, pies and stock cubes. The *normal* lifespan of a chicken is 14–20 years.

Slaughter also awaits male birds who are obviously useless for egg production.

Even if hens are lucky enough to be 'free-range' and are enjoying a relatively natural life in a farmyard, male chicks, not required for laying, are castrated by administering female hormones and then reared as capons for the table. Capon meat is not popular in Britain however and most male chicks are suffocated after hatching like the male chicks from battery farms.

Free-range hens are killed when their laying days are over as it is uneconomic for the farmer to keep non-productive birds.

Besides the death and suffering involved in commercial egg production, many vegans abstain from eating eggs because they view them as a potential 'life' and are repulsed at the thought of consuming the products of a fellow creature's reproductive cycle.

## Bees and honey

Honey is produced from flower nectar by the labours of bees who store it in their hive during the summer, to ensure a supply of food during the winter and spring months when little nectar is to be found.

Good beekeepers look after their bees well, protecting them from predators such as wasps and poisonous insecticides, and preventing swarming which kills thousands of bees.

A healthy bee colony produces honey way beyond its own requirements for the winter — approximately 2–3 times as much as the bees need. Provided the bees have been well cared for and not exploited by the beekeper, this surplus honey may be easily removed without any detriment to the bees.

Unfortunately 'humanely' produced honey forms only a minimal percentage of that which finds its way onto the shelves of supermarkets and health stores. Most back-yard beekeepers keep bees for the pleasure it gives them to be in harmony with nature rather than commercial gain and will usually eat it themselves or give it away to friends.

Honey is not necessary to good nutrition and if eaten in excess, can be just as detrimental to health as sugar. It does however, contain many minerals and no additives, is easily digested and is claimed to have therapeutic properties.

Vegans abstain from eating honey as in commercial production, too much honey may be taken from the hive which necessitates feeding the bees with white sugar syrup to see them through the winter. In some cases the whole hive may be killed after the honey has been collected to reduce the expense of having to keep the bees over the non honey-producing winter months.

As most honey is not produced 'humanely' in my opinion, and so as not to exclude many vegans from trying my recipes, I have not included honey.


## Other products

Many vegans do not wear or use leather, wool, furs, silk or ivory as they feel the selective breeding policies (e.g., mink farming) and manner of death (e.g., elephant slaughter by poaching for their tusks) is an unnecessary evil.

Also, the majority of toiletries, cosmetics, perfumes, washing powders and drugs used daily, either contain products which have been obtained from animals (e.g., tallow in soap from beef fat; lard in face cream from pig fat; whale oil in shampoos, toothpastes and ointments; musk and other perfumes from the anus and genital organs of civet cats, musk deers, musk rats and whales) or have been tested on animals under controlled laboratory conditions which can involve pain, stress and eventual death (e.g., the Draize eye test where rabbits are restrained and have concentrated detergents, bleaches, hair sprays etc., dripped into their eyes for several days resulting in ulceration and eventual blindness).

Use of such products is unnecessary as many alternatives are widely available which rely on plant products and are not tested on animals. The demand for these is increasing due to mass advertising campaigns by various anti-vivisection groups and lists of cruelty-free products are obtainable from them (see p. 301) and from the Vegan and Vegetarian Societies.

### Zoos and circuses

Most vegans boycott circuses and zoos because even though some species are saved from extinction by them, the animals are removed from their natural environments and may be kept in overcrowded, dirty and stressful conditions. I personally feel that animals deserve more respect and reject their use for entertainment in this way and the resulting ridicule they endure.

I hope that this book, by covering every aspect of veganism in detail, offering practical advice and providing easily prepared, delicious recipes, will answer all the questions you may have about the vegan way of life. To everyone, everywhere, whatever you eat, whatever you believe in, may this comprehensive handbook prove invaluable in your search for a compassionate way of life.

# 2

# VEGAN NUTRITION

It is one thing to give up all animal products but quite another to know what to eat instead. A study performed in America (1982) showed that although most vegetarians and vegans have a better knowledge of nutrition than the average omnivore, many are ignorant about the nutrient content of their diet and hold scientifically unsound views about foods and health.

Although our digestive system is remarkably good at sifting through any food we give it and extracting the nutrients we need, good nutritional practices are important to ensure a well-balanced diet. Food science and nutrition is by no means a simple subject. Most textbooks on nutrition are highly scientific and incomprehensible to the average reader. However, in the following section, I have tried to explain the sources of essential nutrients for vegans as simply as possible using very basic scientific terms only if they help to explain the concepts being discussed. I hope that this detailed account will dispel the common misconceptions about vegan nutrition.

**Protein**

The exact amount of protein required by the body depends on a person's age, sex and physical activity but the recommended daily allowance of 50–90 g (2–3 oz) will supply more than enough to meet adult requirements. Recent research carried out on races who consume far less than this and are still fit and healthy has led to some sources suggesting that this figure may be too high.

Protein has two main functions in the body: it is used as a building and repair material for tissues and organs (e.g., skin, hair, muscles, liver); it is also used in the formation of hormones, enzymes and antibodies.

Protein in excess of these requirements is either used as a source of energy and body heat or is stored as fat. As proteins are the most expensive items in the diet it is uneconomic and wasteful to consume more than the body needs when carbohydrate foods are the cheapest energy giving foods available (see p. 30).

### What are proteins?

Proteins are made up of substances called *amino-acids*. There are over 20 different amino-acids found in protein foods. Some of them can be made by the body but there are eight which can not and have to be obtained from food. These are the *essential amino-acids* and their chemical names are leucine, isoleucine, tryptophan, lysine, methionine, threonine, valine and phenylalanine. (Growing children also require two further essential amino-acids: histidine and arginine).

Animal proteins such as meat and dairy foods contain essential amino acids in very similar proportions to those found in human tissues, muscles and organs. Therefore when animal proteins are broken down in the body during digestion, the essential amino-acids they contain can be used by the human body very effectively with little or no wastage. The term used to describe the percentage of protein which is actually available to the body is *net protein utilisation* (NPU) or *biological value*. Proteins which have a high NPU contain amino-acids which closely correspond to the human tissues, muscles and organs that they are required to build. Eggs and human breast milk have the highest NPU ratings of all foods and are therefore classified as 'perfect' protein.

In vegan protein foods, one or more of the essential amino-acids is present in a disproportionately small amount. These amino-acids are called *limiting amino-acids* because they reduce the NPU of that protein. Soya beans* are an

* Although soya beans do contain the eight essential amino-acids in good proportions, they have a rather smaller amount of methionine which may act as a limiting amino-acid in some cases. It is probably advisable to complement them with nuts or grains to maximise the nutritive value.

21

exception to this rule however as they do contain all eight essential amino-acids in good proportions and have a very high NPU. Tofu (soya bean curd) and rice also have a NPU which is similar to that of poultry and cheese and are near 'perfect' proteins.

### Complementary proteins

It is possible to get all the essential amino-acids from one vegan protein food such as lentils or hazelnuts but you would need to eat twice as much of that food to get all the amino-acids in the correct proportions. Excess amino-acids would be used for energy and therefore nutritionally wasted.

However, because the limiting amino-acid in one vegan protein may be in excess in another, when the two are combined the NPU is increased. For example, pulses (beans and lentils) contain a lot of the amino-acid lysine but not very much tryptophan whereas grains (rice, wheat, millet etc.) contain a lot of tryptophan and not very much lysine. So if pulses and grains are combined the deficiencies in one will be made up for by the other.

Combining two nutritionally complementary proteins in this way is called *protein complementarity*, and enables vegans to produce dishes which are equally nutritious as meat or dairy foods without having to eat large quantities of food. It also dispels the notion that protein has to come from a single item of food that forms the core of the meal. In a well-balanced vegan diet, everything on the plate will contribute some protein so that the body's needs are satisfied. The best complementary proteins are: *grains* eaten with *pulses*; and *nuts/seeds* eaten with *pulses*. Some proteins in nuts and grains are also complementary (see Fig. 1).

As the body does not store proteins for very long it is advisable to eat a good range of complementary amino-acids *at each meal*. (Obviously the occasional meal that does not contain all the essential amino-acids will not do any harm.)

This is not as difficult as it sounds and, with a bit of practice, soon becomes habit rather than chore. Baked beans on toast; muesli with soya milk; peanut butter sandwiches; soya milk rice pudding, are all everyday examples of complementary proteins which you probably already eat without even thinking about it.

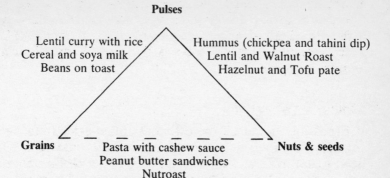

**Pulses**

Lentil curry with rice — Hummus (chickpea and tahini dip)
Cereal and soya milk — Lentil and Walnut Roast
Beans on toast — Hazelnut and Tofu pate

**Grains** — **Nuts & seeds**

Pasta with cashew sauce
Peanut butter sandwiches
Nutroast

—— Good complementarity — most foods in each group contain complementary proteins
– – – Less complementarity — not all foods in each group contain complementary proteins

**Fig. 1.** Vegan protein complementarity

## Using protein efficiently in the body

In order to utilise protein efficiently it is also advisable to include carbohydrate foods in the meal. Carbohydrates prevent amino-acids being wasted as energy and stop them from being converted into urea and excreted in urine.

Proteins are therefore best if eaten as part of a complete food that contains carbohydrate and other nutrients as well. In the vegan diet this is easily achieved because protein sources such as lentils, beans and grains also contain carbohydrate. The examples of complementary proteins above all contain carbohydrates.

## Vegan protein sources

Vegan protein is obtained from four main sources — grains, pulses, nuts and seeds. These can be supplemented with sprouted beans or grains and vegetables which also contain protein. Nuts are a rich source of protein and supply the sulphur-containing amino-acid methionine which is not commonly found in plant foods. For economic reasons it is probably advisable to base your meals on grains and pulses and eat nuts as often as possible to supplement them.

Provided mixtures of proteins are included at every meal in either the main course or desert the vegan diet will easily meet

23

and exceed the daily protein requirement of the body.

*Summary*

**1** Adults need 50–90 g (2–3 oz) protein daily for growth and repair of tissues and the formation of hormones, enzymes and antibodies.
**2** Proteins are made up of amino-acids, eight of which are essential as they cannot be made by the body. The essential amino-acids should ideally be included in every meal.
**3** When two or more vegan proteins are combined their net protein utilisation or biological value is greatly increased.
The best complementary proteins are *grains with pulses* and *nuts with pulses*.
**4** Proteins are more available to the body when the meal contains carbohydrate.
**5** Vegan protein sources are: nuts, grains, pulses, seeds, beansprouts and vegetables. The most nutritionally complete sources are soya beans, tofu, soya milk, rice and nuts.

## Fats, Cholesterol and Slimming

Fats and carbohydrates work together in the body to provide energy in the form of calories. The daily requirement of calories for an adult ranges from 2200 to 3500 depending on age, sex and physical activities. Approximately 30–40% of these calories come from fat. Too much fat in proportion to carbohydrate can cause nausea and vomiting; therefore fats should always be eaten with carbohydrate foods (e.g. bread and margarine).

Besides giving us energy, fats have many other functions. They are stored in the body to act as insulation and keep us warm and act as a fuel reserve if we have no food. They also provide fat-soluble vitamins, help to regulate blood flow and are a major component of cell membranes, body tissues, vital organs, nerve fibres and capillaries.

Fats are a very concentrated food so they satisfy the appetite longer than other foods by slowing down digestion. They also make food more palatable and easier to swallow.

### What are fats?

All fats are made up of substances known as *triglycerides*.

Triglycerides consist of one molecule of glycerine linked to three molecules of fatty acid. There are three types of fatty acid and the difference between one fat and another depends largely on which fatty acids it contains. The fatty acids themselves are made up of hydrogen, carbon and oxygen. They have their own characteristic properties depending on the amount of hydrogen they contain.

*Saturated fatty-acids* are found predominantly in animal fats such as lard, butter and suet but are also present in coconut and palm oil. The more saturated the fat, the more hydrogen atoms it contains and the more solid it is at room temperature. Vegetable fats can be made more saturated by a process called *hydrogenation*. This is when hydrogen gas is bubbled through the vegetable fat causing it to become saturated and harden. This process is used in the manufacture of vegetable margarines and solid vegetable fats. Despite being labelled 'high in polyunsaturates', most margarines contain about 50% saturated fat.

Saturated fats can be made from carbohydrate in the body and are therefore not necessary in the diet.

*Mono-unsaturated fatty-acids* are found in nuts and some fruits. They can also be manufactured by the body from carbohydrate. They contain less hydrogen than saturated fatty acids. Olive oil is particularly high in mono-unsaturates.

*Polyunsaturated fatty-acids* are found predominantly in vegetable oils such as safflower, sunflower, sesame, soya and corn oil. They contain far less hydrogen than saturated fatty acids and are usually liquid at room temperature.

There are several different polyunsaturated fatty acids, three of which cannot be made by the body and must therefore be included in the diet. These are called *essential fatty acids* and are sometimes referred to collectively as *vitamin F* (see p. 44). Their names are *arachidonic acid*, *linoleic acid* and *linolenic acid*.

Essential fatty acids are vital components of cell membranes, nerve fibres and brain cells. They work with vitamin D to facilitate the absorption of calcium and phosphorus from food which are then deposited in bones and teeth. They also distribute fat soluble vitamins A, E and K round the bloodstream, promote the growth of beneficial intestinal bacteria, nourish the skin keeping it soft and supple and are vital for the correct functioning of the adrenal glands, reproductive organs and thyroid gland.

The amounts required daily are very small and as they are found in abundance in plant oils, nuts and seeds, they are unlikely to be deficient in a vegan diet. Arachidonic acid can be made in the body from linoleic acid but it is still advisable to have a dietary supply.

Besides fatty acids, fats contain two other very important substances called lecithin and cholesterol.

*Lecithin* is made up of glycerol, polyunsaturated fatty acids and the mineral element phosphorus.

Lecithin is a fat emulsifier, that is, it breaks up fats keeping them liquid and distributing them round the body so they cannot be deposited in organs or arteries. It is a component of bile and is stored in the gall bladder where it prevents cholesterol from hardening and forming gallstones. It is also a significant factor in preventing cholesterol from being deposited in the arteries which may lead to heart disease.

Lecithin is essential for the health of the skin and nails and is a component of the fatty protective covering around nerve fibres. It acts as an antioxidant thus preventing fats going rancid and it is important to the health of the bacteria in the gut thereby preventing diarrhoea and other bowel disorders.

Lecithin is also a source of choline and inositol — (B-complex vitamins, see p. 36), vitamins E and K and the mineral element zinc. The best vegan sources of lecithin are polyunsaturated oils (especially soya oil), soya beans and all soya products (see p. 96).

The correct balance of lecithin and cholesterol in the body is essential.

*Cholesterol* is made from fatty acids and alcohol. Despite its bad reputation, it is actually essential for life and is a component of all cells. Cholesterol is vital for the production of bile salts, and adrenal and sexual hormones. It is manufactured in the body by the liver and is therefore not necessary in the diet.

Contrary to popular belief, cholesterol does not contain any calories so consuming it will not make you put on weight. Stating the cholesterol content of foods actually says nothing and implies nothing about the calorie content of that food or the amount of fat in it. Many manufacturers exploit peoples ignorance by stating the absence of cholesterol as a selling point.

Cholesterol combines with protein to form a substance called a *Lipoprotein*. There are several types of lipoprotein but the two main ones are *low density lipoprotein* (the 'bad' form of cholesterol that tends to accumulate in the arteries) and *high density lipoprotein* (the 'good' form of cholesterol that carries cholesterol away from the arteries to the liver where it is broken down and excreted).

An excess or imbalance of the wrong type of cholesterol can cause health problems. It has been shown that people with high levels of low density lipoprotein in their blood are the ones most at risk from heart disease.

Cholesterol is found only in animal foods such as eggs, milk, seafood and butter. Consuming these foods *does not necessarily* increase a persons risk from heart disease as the liver regulates its output accordingly.

However, there are several factors which *do* increase the level of cholesterol in the blood and significantly increase a persons risk of heart disease:

(i)   The consumption of saturated fatty acids raises the level of low density lipoprotein cholesterol in the blood. The fact that animal foods which contain saturated fat also contain cholesterol has led to the misguided assumption that cholesterol-containing foods raise cholesterol levels in the body and cause heart disease. It is not the cholesterol that raises blood cholesterol, but the *saturated fat* the foods contain.

(ii)   High levels of *body fat increases* blood cholesterol so obese people are more likely to suffer from heart disease.

Conversely, factors which lower blood cholesterol levels include:

(i)   The consumption of polyunsaturated fatty acids, especially arachidonic acid.

(ii)   Increasing fibre intake, as fibre has been found to bind to cholesterol enhancing its excretion.

(iii)   A diet high in vitamin E, lecithin, calcium, magnesium and zinc.

(iv)   Regular exercise not only lowers the level of low density lipoprotein but increases the level of high density lipoproteins.

The vegan diet contains a lot of unsaturated fat, fibre, vitamin E, lecithin, calcium, magnesium and zinc, and vegans generally tend to enjoy exercise and not be overweight; they are therefore less likely to suffer from heart disease as a result of excess cholesterol in the blood.

It is worth noting however, that *palm* and *coconut* oil, even though they are vegetable fats, will still raise low density lipoprotein cholesterol levels in the blood because they are very saturated.

As mixed vegetable cooking oils and solid vegetable fats (both of which are often labelled 'no cholesterol') probably contain some palm oil, they are likely to raise blood cholesterol when consumed. For this reason it is probably advisable to stick to 100% pure polyunsaturated oils such as sunflower.

## Vegan fat sources

Vegan sources of fat are nuts, seeds, margarine, cereals, avocado pears and vegetable oil — all of which supply essential fatty acids and fat soluble vitamins.

## Buying oils

*Cold-pressed oils* are extracted slowly from the seed by a hydraulic press and then filtered. This retains all the original vitamins and minerals from the seed as well as the flavour and natural aroma. As they contain no preservatives or additives cold-pressed oils tend to be darker in colour and may have a sediment at the bottom of the bottle. Oils which are labelled 'virgin' are the most pure as they contain only oil from the first pressing of the seed and have not been mixed with oils from a second or third pressing. Cold-pressing is usually used for soft, oily seeds such as olive, sesame and sunflower. They will keep for 6 months or longer if they are stored in dark bottles.

*Oils from hard seeds* such as safflower, grains such as corn and beans such as soya are more difficult to extract. They are usually pressed in a screw press which exerts a greater force than a hydraulic press. The seeds to be pressed are steamed first but even so the amount of oil extracted is quite low and they are expensive.

*Processed oils* such as those found in supermarkets are extracted at high temperatures using petroleum based solvents to give a higher yield of oil. They are then refined to remove the solvent, filtered and bleached. Unfortunately the heat and the solvent destroys many of the vitamins and minerals in the oil and removes any lecithin present so they are nutritionally inferior to cold-pressed oils. Refined oils are paler in colour, have no characteristic aroma or flavour and may contain additives and antioxidants to prevent rancidity.

Excessive temperatures cause oxidation of oils making

them go rancid. Rancid oils are toxic if eaten. Vitamin E which is present in cold-pressed oils is a natural antioxidant. This is removed during refining however, so refined oils are likely to go rancid unless they contain additives.

When buying oils choose a good quality cold-pressed unrefined oil (Table 1).

**Table 1.** Types of vegetable oils and their properties.

---

*Olive*
A strong, dark, aromatic oil with characteristic flavour. Contains least impurities of all oils. Very digestible; facilitates absorption of vitamins A, D, E and K. Good for deep frying as it gets hotter than other oils before going rancid. Best oil for salads. Tonic effect on digestion and said to cure numerous disorders.

*Peanut (groundnut)*
Highly unsaturated. Best known vegetable source of vitamin $B_5$ (pantothenic acid) and vitamin E. Bland oil so good for all cooking. Can be clarified and reused several times.

*Corn (maize)*
Good for salads and baking. Used in margarine manufacture.

*Safflower*
The most polyunsaturated oil of all — contains approximately 90% unsaturated fatty acids. Light oil, good for salads and cooking.

*Sesame*
The second most polyunsaturated next to safflower. Extremely nutritious. Does not go rancid even at very high temperatures so ideal for deep frying. Used in Oriental cookery.

*Sunflower*
Very easily digested. Light, nutty flavour; less greasy than most oils so ideal for all cooking. A good general purpose oil.

*Soya*
Used predominantly for margarine manufacture. Very nutritious; good source of vitamin E. Characteristic flavour makes it ideal for deep frying — used a lot in Chinese cookery. Another general purpose oil.

---

## Slimming

There has been a growing trend over the past few decades to consume fat in excess of the body's requirement. This leads to weight gain and possible obesity with all the associated risks of high blood pressure, diabetes and heart disease.

The vegan diet can help significantly in weight loss as it is low in fat and high in fibre so the body feels more satisfied after eating and blood sugar levels are stabilised reducing cravings for more food. Fruit, vegetables, pulses, grains and tofu are all low calorie foods with little or no fat which form the basis of a slimming diet.

Anyone slimming seriously should consult a doctor before embarking on *any* diet, but in general the higher calorie foods to cut down on in the vegan diet are nuts, oils, margarine and dried fruit.

### Summary

1  Fats supply the body with energy, warmth and fat soluble vitamins; regulate blood flow; are a component of cell membranes, body tissues, vital organs, nerve fibres and capillaries; satisfy the appetite longer than other foods and make food more palatable.
2  Adults require 2200–3500 calories a day, 30–40% of which should come from fat.
3  Fats contain fatty acids which may be *saturated* (mainly animal), *mono-unsaturated* (nuts and fruit) or *polyunsaturated* (mainly vegetable). Polyunsaturated fats cannot be manufactured by the body and as three of them are essential it is important to include them in the diet.
4  Saturated fats *raise* blood cholesterol levels when consumed whereas polyunsaturated fats significantly *lower* it. Cholesterol-containing foods do not necessarily raise blood cholesterol when consumed.
5  Vegan fat sources are nuts, seeds, margarine, cereals and vegetable oils which should be cold-pressed and unrefined to maximise nutritive value.
6  When slimming, eat more low fat foods (fruit, vegetables, pulses, grains and tofu) and cut down on high fat foods (nuts, oils and margarine).

## Carbohydrates

Carbohydrates are the body's main source of energy and provide 50–60% of the calories required daily by adults.

Most carbohydrate is used for energy but some may be converted to *fatty-acids* or *glycogen* which are stored in the body fat and liver, respectively, as fuel reserves.

Carbohydrates are essential for the efficient use of protein by the body, and in high fat diets where nausea may occur if the fat:carbohydrate ratio is imbalanced.

Many carbohydrates, especially cereals and pulses, also supply B-vitamins, minerals and dietary fibre.

## What are carbohydrates?

There are three types of carbohydrate found in food, namely, sugar, starch and cellulose (fibre). Carbohydrates are made up of glucose, which is a sugar, and their properties depend on the number of glucose molecules they contain.

*Monosaccharides* (simple sugars) e.g. glucose and fructose, occur naturally in fruits and vegetables. During digestion most carbohydrates are broken down to glucose which is absorbed very quickly into the bloodstream providing energy. Fructose is the 'sweetest' sugar known.

*Disaccharides* (double-sugars) which are made from two monosaccharides joined together. Sucrose (from glucose and fructose) occurs naturally in some fruits and vegetables especially sugar cane and sugar beat. White sugar is pure sucrose.

Maltose (from two glucose molecules) is produced during the digestion of starch in the body and also when grains are germinated for use in the brewing industry. Malt extract consists of maltose.

*Polysaccharides*: Starches are polysaccharides made from hundreds of glucose molecules joined together. When cooked, starches absorb water, swell up and eventually gelatinize, making them easily digestible. Starches are found in cereals, pulses and some vegetables. They are broken down to their component glucose molecules when digested.

Cellulose is a polysaccharide made up of thousands of glucose molecules. It is found in the cell walls and fibrous parts of plants. Cellulose cannot be digested by humans but absorbs water and adds bulk to the faeces assisting their elimination from the body. Cellulose is more commonly known as dietary fibre.

Pectin is another polysaccharide found in fruits and vegetables. It helps to make jams and preserves set and is thought to reduce the absorption of cholesterol by the body, thereby helping to reduce the risks of heart disease (see p. 27).

## Advantages of unrefined carbohydrates

The main sources of carbohydrate in the vegan diet are unrefined polysaccharides. These are bulky foods which

31

contain a lot of fibre (cellulose) so they take longer to digest than monosaccharides or disaccharides. This means there is less tendency to overeat and glucose is released very slowly into the bloodstream preventing the risks of diabetes, high blood pressure and obesity. In addition, the high fibre content causes food to pass very quickly through the digestive system reducing the risks of constipation and bowel cancer. As they are unrefined, these carbohydrates also contain other nutrients — protein, vitamins and minerals.

Refined carbohydrates such as white sugar, white flour and polished rice have a lower nutritive value because vitamins and minerals are removed during processing. They are basically a source of calories with little or no other nutrients and are often termed 'empty-calorie' foods.

High sugar diets are commonly associated with increased tooth decay and hyperactivity in children. As white sugar contains no fibre it is not satisfying and leads to cravings for more food. If eaten in excess it may cause diabetes and obesity.

Most vegans prefer to avoid sugary foods but if a sweetener is required it is preferable to use molasses, malt extract, maple syrup or dried fruit purée as these are better sources of nutrients.

### Vegan carbohydrate sources

A well balanced vegan diet will supply all the energy required from carbohydrate in grains, bread, pasta, pastry, pulses, breakfast cereals, nuts and root vegetables. Such foods also contain fibre, protein, vitamins, minerals and some fat.

### Summary

**1** Carbohydrates supply the body with energy, are essential for the efficient use of protein and fat and may supply B-vitamins, minerals and fibre.
**2** Adults require 2200–3500 calories a day — carbohydrates supply 50–60%.
**3** The three types of carbohydrate are *sugar*, *starch* and *cellulose* which are all made of glucose.
**4** There are two types of sugar — monosaccharides and dissacharides — both of which occur naturally in fruit and vegetables.

**5** Starch and cellulose are polysaccharides found in grains, pulses, fruit and vegetables. Starch is broken down to its component glucose molecules during digestion and these are released very slowly into the bloodstream. Cellulose is indigestible and assists elimination.

**6** Unrefined polysaccharides have a higher nutritional value than refined carbohydrates and may reduce the risks of obesity, diabetes, high blood pressure, constipation, bowel cancer and tooth decay.

**7** Vegan carbohydrate sources are grains, flour products, pulses, nuts and root vegetables.


## Vitamins

Vitamins are substances required in minute quantities by the body to maintain health and assist growth. Some vitamins can be manufactured by the body but they may not be absorbed in the quantities necessary for health so the major source of all vitamins is food. Deficiencies of vitamins lead to specific recognisable symptoms which usually clear up on treatment with the vitamin in question.

There are over 20 vitamins altogether, each having its own specific function within the body although they usually work in conjunction with other vitamins and minerals. The functions of 13 vitamins are well-documented but the others are still being researched. Two substances called *choline* and *inositol* are classified as vitamins but strictly speaking they are not as they are produced in the body in sufficient quantities to maintain health — however, under certain conditions their production may be reduced and a dietary supply required.

*Para-aminobenzoic acid* (PABA) is also classed as a vitamin because it is necessary for micro-organism growth and is a component of folic acid, one of the B-vitamins, and although research has not yet conclusively shown that PABA is essential for human growth, it usually finds its way into vitamin tables.


### Classification

*Fat soluble vitamins* are less sensitive to heat and more stable during cooking but are destroyed slowly on exposure to light and air. They are stored in the body in the liver or fatty

33

tissues; therefore short-term deficiencies are not too harmful. Fat soluble vitamins are poisonous if eaten in excess.

*Water soluble vitamins* are extremely sensitive to heat, light and air and are easily destroyed on cooking. They cannot generally be stored in the body therefore a daily supply is essential. Any excess water soluble vitamins are excreted in the urine.

### Supplements

Vitamin tablets should not be necessary in a well balanced vegan diet (with the exception of vitamin $B_{12}$; see p. 47). In certain cases however, it may be necessary to take some supplements, for example during pregnancy or when recovering from an illness.

Vitamins are required in extremely small quantities by the body and are only found in minute quantities in foods. Therefore, rather than being measured in grams they are measured in either *milligrams* mg, (1/1000g) or *micrograms,* μg (1/1000 000 g).

### Absorption

Not all the vitamins present in food will be absorbed by the body. Some vitamins may be bound to substances that are indigestible which causes them to be excreted from the body without being utilised. People who have illnesses that prevent them from digesting fats will not be able to absorb fat soluble vitamins properly and may be deficient unless supplements are taken.

Fat soluble vitamins are also unavailable to the body if the diet contains mineral oils of any kind. Mineral oils are commonly used to wash dried fruit such as raisins, sultanas etc. and give them a shiny appearance. They are also used as a laxative. Mineral oils absorb fat soluble vitamins and carry them out of the body.

It is therefore vital to include high intakes of all the vitamins in the daily diet to allow for lack of absorption.

### Enemies of vitamins

Water soluble vitamins and, to a lesser degree, fat soluble vitamins, are sensitive to heat, air and light and may be destroyed on cooking. Water soluble vitamins are also particularly sensitive to chemicals added to cooking water such as bicarbonate of soda.

Vitamins may also be affected by drugs such as aspirin, oral contraceptives, caffeine, nicotine, antibiotics and alcohol. People who smoke, drink a lot of coffee or alcohol, take aspirins or antibiotics regularly or are on the Pill are therefore advised to increase their vitamin intake.

Diets high in refined carbohydrate will increase the body's need for B-vitamins that are used to metabolise carbohydrate. High fat diets increase the need for vitamin E.

## Vegans and vitamins

The majority of essential vitamins are well represented in a wide range of vegetables, fruits, beansprouts, pulses, nuts, grains and seeds so deficiencies are extremely unlikely.

There is some controversy however, over vitamins $B_{12}$ and D as these are generally only found in animal foods. Vegans can easily obtain their bodily requirements of both these vitamins.

Table 2 summarizes the best vegan sources of the 13 most widely known vitamins, and inositol, choline and PABA; describes briefly how they are used in the body, and lists the deficiency symptoms for reference.

## Vitamin D

From the age of 5 years we require 2.5 µg/day of vitamin D. This extremely small amount is vital to maintain the calcium and phosphorus levels of the blood, facilitate the absorption of calcium from the small intestine and for the formation of bones and teeth. Vitamin D is also required for the health of the nervous system, skin, heart and thyroid gland.

DEFICIENCY

Deficiencies of vitamin D are especially serious during infancy, pregnancy and lactation, when the daily requirement increases to 10 µg.

Infants who are deficient in vitamin D may suffer irreversible deformities of the skeleton known as rickets where the bones become too weak to support the body.

**Table 2.** Summary of vitamins; their functions and vegan sources. F Sol, Fat soluble; W Sol, Water soluble; HS, heat stability.

| Vitamin (chemical name) | RDI | Function in body | Affected by | Deficiency symptoms | Vegan sources |
|---|---|---|---|---|---|
| A (Retinol) F Sol. HS good | 750 µg | Normal growth; health of skin, hair, bones, teeth, gums, mucous membranes and eyes. Helps body resist infection. Essential for sight in dim light. Stored in liver which may contain 1 year supply. Toxic in large doses. | | Sore mouth and gums, low resistance to disease, dandruff, skin problems, brittle nails, night-blindness; if severe — complete blindness. | Does not occur naturally in any plant foods but *carotene*, a substance found in plant foods, can be converted into vitamin A by the body. Sources of carotene are carrots, tomatoes, dried prunes and apricots, spinach, green vegetables, beansprouts and margarine. |
| B$_1$ (Thiamin) W Sol. HS moderate | 0.9–1.4 mg | Normal growth. Release of energy from carbohydrate. Correct function of nervous system, muscles, heart, brain. Health of ears, eyes and hair. Works with vitamins B$_2$ and B$_6$. | Coffee Alcohol The Pill Smoking Drugs Bicarbonate of soda | Loss of appetite, depression, fatigue, indigestion, constipation, nervous disorders; if severe, Beri-Beri results. | Yeast extract, wheatgerm, tofu, Brazil nuts, peanuts, soya flour, oatmeal, lentils, beans, bread, wholemeal flour, brown rice, beansprouts. |

| Vitamin | Amount | Function | Enemies | Deficiency | Sources |
|---|---|---|---|---|---|
| B$_2$ (Riboflavin) W Sol. HS good | 1.3–1.7 mg | Vital for production of enzymes used for release of energy from carbohydrate. Normal growth and reproduction. Helps make antibodies and red blood cells. Health of skin, hair, nails and mucous membranes. Works with vitamins B$_1$ and B$_6$. | Alcohol The Pill Bicarbonate of soda | Cracks in the corner of the mouth, sore sensitive eyes, inflamed tongue, poor skin, nervous problems. | Yeast extract, almonds, pulses, wheatgerm, mushrooms, green vegetables, dried fruit, beansprouts. |
| B$_3$ (Niacin) W Sol. HS good | 15–18 mg | Release of energy from carbohydrates. Health of skin, brain, liver, tissues, nervous system. Essential for production of sex hormones. Aids circulation and acid production in stomach. Helps body use protein, iron and calcium. Can be made in body from amino-acid *tryptophan*. | Coffee Alcohol | Mouth ulcers, skin disorders, nervous problems, diarrhoea, constipation; if severe, pellagra results which can be fatal. | Yeast extract, peanuts, soya flour, tofu, pulses, bread, wholemeal flour, almonds, mushrooms, brown rice. |

**Table 2.** (contd)

| Vitamin (chemical name) | RDI | Function in body | Affected by | Deficiency symptoms | Vegan sources |
|---|---|---|---|---|---|
| $B_5$ (Pantothenic acid) W Sol. HS poor | 10 mg | Normal growth, cell and nerve development, release of energy from carbohydrate and fat. Healthy skin. Acts as a detoxifier. Vital to the production of antibodies and correct functioning of adrenal glands. Can be manufactured in the small intestines. | Coffee Alcohol The Pill | Skin and blood disorders, insomnia, depression, fatigue, pains in the feet. Deficiency extremely unlikely. | All plant foods especially peanuts, mushrooms, grains, wheatgerm, pulses. |
| $B_6$ (Pyridoxine) W Sol. HS good | 2.0 mg | Formation of haemoglobin and antibodies in blood. Metabolises protein and fat. Healthy skin, blood, muscles, nerves. Needed for the correct absorption of vitamin $B_{12}$ and production of hydrochloric acid in stomach that aids digestion. Helps in | Alcohol The Pill | Anaemia, depression, muscle cramp, nervous and skin disorders. | Yeast extract, walnuts, beans, soya flour, tofu, lentils, hazelnuts, bananas, bread, wholemeal flour. |

| Vitamin | Amount | Functions | Destroyers | Deficiency | Sources |
|---|---|---|---|---|---|
| B₁₂ (Cobalamin) W Sol. HS good | 1–3µg | production of vitamin B₃ from tryptophan. Used to treat menstrual problems in women. Works with vitamin B₁ and B₂. Half total body content stored in liver where vital for production of haemoglobin. Essential for growth, cell division, energy release from carbohydrate, health of nervous and reproductive systems. Works with all other B-vitamins, vitamins A, C, E and minerals cobalt and calcium. | The Pill Alcohol | Tiredness, sore tongue, indigestion; if severe — causes abnormal blood formation that leads to megaloblastic anaemia, nervous disorders that lead to degeneration of the spine and infertility in women. | Fortified yeast extract, fortified soya milk, miso, kelp, tempeh, soya sauce, alfalfa sprouts, beer, wine, dietary supplements. |
| H (Biotin— member of the B-group) W Sol. HS good | 150–300 µg | Involved in enzyme systems and cell growth. Promotes healthy skin, hair and nerves. Essential to health of sweat glands, bone marrow and sex glands. Helps metabolise fats, protein and carbohydrate. Can be produced in intestines. Works with vitamins A, B₂, B₃, B₆. | Alcohol The Pill | Poor appetite, exhaustion, dermatitis, muscle pains. Deficiency in vegans very unlikely. | Bananas, yeast extract, nuts, pulses, fruit, vegetables. |

**Table 2.** (contd)

| Vitamin (chemical name) | RDI | Function in body | Affected by | Deficiency symptoms | Vegan sources |
|---|---|---|---|---|---|
| M (Folic acid — member of the B-group) W Sol. HS poor | 200 µg | Formation of red blood cells and body cells. Helps circulation. Health of skin, glands, liver, stomach. Metabolises protein and carbohydrate. Close relationship with vitamin $B_{12}$. Extremely important for pregnant women. Deficiency in vegans very unlikely. | The Pill Aspirin Alcohol | Diarrhoea, inflamed tongue, stomach problems. If severe — anaemia and degeneration of the nervous system. | Green vegetables, oranges, pulses, nuts, bread, bananas. |
| Choline (member of the B-group) W Sol. HS good | 650 mg | Essential to prevent fat being deposited in organs of the body; liver, heart, kidneys, brain, blood vessels. Prevents formation of gallstones and lowers blood cholesterol. Vital for proper nerve functioning. Health of hair and thymus gland. | | Possible gall-stones, kidney problems and heart disease as a result of excess fat in organs and blood vessels. Also nervous disorders and possible dementia. | Best source is *Lecithin* (see p. 26). Also wheatgerm, soya beans, asparagus, cabbage, carrots, peas, spinach, potatoes, sprouts, turnip, brewers yeast, pulses. |

| Vitamin | Amount | Functions in the body | Enemy | Deficiency / Excess symptoms | Best sources |
|---|---|---|---|---|---|
|  |  | Very little is excreted and the daily requirement is high when compared to other vitamins. Made in the body from amino-acid *methionine* so it is essential to include this in the diet (best source is nuts). |  |  |  |
| Inositol (member of the B-group) W Sol. HS good | 1 g | Associated with choline and Biotin. Aids metabolism of fat, prevents fat being deposited in organs and lowers blood cholesterol. Found in the brain, nerves and spinal cord. Health of eyes, heart, digestive tract, skin, hair, muscles and kidneys. Can be made in body from *glucose*. | Caffeine | Constipation, eczema, eye problems, heart problems, anxiety, irritability, hyperactivity. Causes fat to be deposited in organs. | Best source is *Lecithin* (see p. 26). Also yeast, wheatgerm, oatmeal, grains, beans, citrus fruit, nuts, molasses, potatoes, peanuts, green vegetables. |
| Para Amino-benzoic Acid (PABA) — member of the B-group W Sol. HS good | Not known | Part of the structure of *folic acid*, this form appears to be necessary for protein metabolism and blood cell formation. Promotes hair growth. Beneficial to the skin; cures vitiligo (lack of |  | Taken in excess, causes nausea, vomiting, itching and possible liver damage. Deficiency symptoms not yet known. | Grains, molasses, wheatgerm, wholemeal flour, bread, yeast extract, green vegetables. |

| Vitamin (chemical name) | RDI | Function in body | Affected by | Deficiency symptoms | Vegan sources |
|---|---|---|---|---|---|
| | | skin pigment in patches on body) if taken with vitamins B₅ and B₆, zinc and manganese; acts as a natural sun screen and protects against skin cancer caused by ultra-violet light. | | | |
| C (Ascorbic Acid) W Sol. HS poor | 30 mg | Maintains health of connective tissue, assists healing of wounds and promotes healthy bone growth. Prevents infections. Vital for normal brain and nerve function and health of skin, teeth, hair, gums, adrenal glands, blood and capillaries. Acts as an antioxidant to stop other substances being destroyed by air. Natural laxative. Increases absorption of iron by the body. | Alcohol The Pill Smoking Aspirin Bicarbonate of soda Anti-histamines | Bleeding gums, sore joints, slow healing of wounds, depression, bruising; if severe — causes scurvy which is fatal. | Citrus fruits, blackcurrants, green vegetables, potatoes, peppers, beansprouts, tomatoes. |

| Vitamin | RDA | Function | Destroyed by | Deficiency | Sources |
|---|---|---|---|---|---|
| D (Calciferol) F Sol. HS good | 2.5 µg | Helps absorption of calcium and its deposition in bones and teeth. Maintains level of calcium and phosphorus in the blood. Health of nervous sytem, heart, skin, thyroid gland. Excess causes too much calcium to be absorbed which leads to kidney damage. Stored in the liver. | | Bone softening and eventually *rickets* in children or *osteomalacia* in adults. | Fortified margarine, fortified soya milk, sunlight. |
| E (Tocopherols — several types known to exist) F Sol. HS Good | 11–15 mg | Component of all cell membranes. Normal growth. Health of muscles especially the heart, adrenal glands, sex glands and pituitary gland. Healthy skin, hair, lungs, nerves, blood vessels. Alleviates fatigue and lowers blood pressure. Reduces blood cholesterol and protects unsaturated fats from oxidation. Prevents destruction of vitamins A, B and C. | Chlorine in water The Pill | No clear deficiency disease but may lead to decreased lifespan of red blood cells, anaemia and reproductive disorders. Deficiency very unlikely in vegans. | Unsaturated vegetable oils, fruit, green vegetables, pulses, nuts, wheatgerm, beansprouts, margarine. |

**Table 2.** (*contd*)

| Vitamin (chemical name) | RDI | Function in body | Affected by | Deficiency symptoms | Vegan sources |
|---|---|---|---|---|---|
| F (Poly-unsaturated fatty Acids — linoleic, linolenic, arachidonic) F Sol. HS good | Not yet known — very small amounts | Work with vitamin D to faciliatate the absorption of calcium and phosphorus. Nourish the skin. Essential for normal functioning of adrenal glands, reproductive organs and thyroid gland. Vital component of cell membranes, nerve fibres and brain cells. Lower blood cholesterol. Cannot be made in body so have to be obtained from food. Easily oxidised and turn rancid if overheated. | | Eczema, dandruff, boils and acne, diarrhoea, weight loss, dry brittle hair and nails, kidney disorders. | Any polyunsaturated oils (e.g. soya, safflower, sunflower, peanut, corn). Some vegan margarines, nuts, grains. |

| | | | | | |
|---|---|---|---|---|---|
| K (Napthaquinone) F Sol. HS good | 0.5–2.0 mg | Essential for blood clotting proteins in liver. Can be produced in the body and absorbed by the bowel so deficiency very unlikely. | Aspirin | Excessive bleeding and haemorrhaging. | Green vegetables, grains, kelp, alfalfa sprouts, soya oil, spinach. |
| P (Bioflavonoids — several types known to exist) W Sol. HS moderate | 50–100 mg | Protects and builds capillaries. Works with vitamin C to keep blood vessels healthy. Minimises bruising. Health of skin, gums, ligaments, bones and teeth. Protects vitamin C from oxidation. | | Decreased capillary resistance which increases risk of infection. | Citrus fruits. Peel and fibrous parts of other fruits especially blackcurrants, grapes, apricots, cherries, plums. Also found in buckwheat. |

References: Brown, S. *Healthy Living Cookbook* (Dorling Kindersley, 1985); Lucas, J.W. *Vegetarian Nutrition* (The Vegetarian Society, 1979); Mervyn, L. *The Vitamins Explained Simply* (Science of Life, Books, 1984); Ministry of Agriculture, Fisheries and Food *Manual of Nutrition* (HMSO 1976); Sanders, T.A.B. & Ellis, F.R. *Vegan Nutrition* (The Vegan Society 1981).

Pregnant and lactating women who are deficient in vitamin D and calcium may suffer from softening of the bones as calcium is drawn from them for breast milk and to form the baby's bones. This condition is known as osteomalacia and is particularly prevalent in women who have had repeated pregnancies and breast fed all their babies. Welfare foods containing vitamin D supplements are available in this country for infants, pregnant and lactating women.

A related condition called osteoporosis may affect elderly people causing their bones to loose calcium, become brittle and break easily.

Excessive doses of vitamin D are not advisable because this will cause more calcium to be absorbed than can be excreted. Excess calcium is deposited in the kidneys; possibly damaging them.

### SOURCES

Vitamin D occurs naturally in meat, fish and dairy produce in the form of *cholecalciferol* or *vitamin $D_3$*. It can also be manufactured in the body from a substance called *ergosterol* which is found in some plant foods, especially yeast. Ergosterol present in the blood is transported to the skin where it absorbs ultra-violet rays from the sun and is converted into *ergocalciferol* or *vitamin $D_2$*.

Sunlight is by far the most important source of vitamin D for the majority of the population including vegans. If the skin is exposed to the sun during the summer months no dietary supplementation is needed as the liver can store enough vitamin D to last over the winter.

All vegan margarines and some brands of soya milk are fortified with vitamin $D_2$ which is manufactured from the ergosterol in cultured yeast. Providing these are included in the diet regularly and the skin is exposed to the sun as much as possible, vegans should have no problems obtaining the recommended allowance.

### VEGAN ETHNIC MINORITY GROUPS

Vitamin D deficiency is a problem amongst some vegan ethnic minority groups in this country; particularly in women and children.

This may be as a result of several factors — low dietary

intake; dark skin pigments that reduce the beneficial effect of ultra voilet light; the social custom of women covering their skin, or genetic factors that appear to reduce vitamin D absorption in some races. In such cases supplements are advisable.

### Vitamin $B_{12}$

Vitamin $B_{12}$ is very unusual because it contains a metal called cobalt in its structure. It can only be made by microorganisms and minute quantities are required for health. 1–3 μg is the recommended daily allowance.

About half the body's vitamin $B_{12}$ is stored in the liver where it is used to produce haemoglobin, an essential component of blood. It is also necessary for correct growth and cell division, energy release from carbohydrate and the health of the nervous and reproductive systems. Vitamin $B_{12}$ works with all the other B-vitamins and vitamins A, C and E in the body and requires adequate cobalt and calcium in the diet in order for it to be absorbed properly.

DEFICIENCY

Deficiencies of vitamin $B_{12}$ are extremely serious and lead to a number of diseases. Early deficiency symptoms are tiredness, breathlessness and indigestion but if allowed to continue, severe deficiencies may lead to megaloblastic anaemia, nervous disorders, degeneration of the spine and infertility (especially in women). Babies that are breastfed by mothers deficient in vitamin $B_{12}$ may suffer brain damage, stunted growth and anaemia.

*Megaloblastic anaemia* is characterised by the formation of abnormally large and unevenly shaped red blood cells which have a shorter lifespan than normal red cells. It may also be caused by a deficiency of folic acid (vitamin M) which has a close relationship with vitamin $B_{12}$. Deficiencies of folic acid also cause anaemia and nervous disorders.

As megaloblastic anaemia can be cured by high doses of folic acid and vegans generally have very high intakes of this vitamin, they are extremely unlikely to suffer from this disease.

In order for vitamin $B_{12}$ to be absorbed properly during digestion it has to bind itself to a substance known as the 'intrinsic factor' which is produced in the small intestine. Some people cannot produce enough of this factor in their bodies so although they may be getting enough vitamin $B_{12}$ in their diet, they cannot absorb it. This condition is called *pernicious anaemia* and is characterised by a drastic fall in the haemoglobin content of the blood; it is linked to serious nervous disorders and eventual degeneration of the spine.

Both the anaemia and the early signs of nervous trouble can be cured by high doses of vitamin $B_{12}$ but if the deficiency is severe the spinal cord will be irreversibly damaged and will probably cause death. Folic acid can also be used to treat pernicious anaemia but it has no effect on the nervous disorders associated with the condition.

SOURCES

Vitamin $B_{12}$ is found in offal, meat and dairy produce which has led to the concern about dietary intake in vegans. However, the sources of vitamin $B_{12}$ available to vegans are many.

*Seaweed*, *alfalfa* and *comfrey* (a herb) are three plants which contain vitamin $B_{12}$. Seaweed and comfrey may provide a useful supplementation to the diet but they are not commonly eaten foods and large amounts are required in order to obtain the daily recommendation. Alfalfa sprouts are delicious in salads and sandwiches but again, large amounts are required.

A Japanese fermented soya bean paste called *miso* also contains vitamin $B_{12}$. It is a more feasible dietary supplement than either comfrey or seaweed as it is more readily available and acceptable to the palate. It can be added to soups, sauces, casseroles, pâtés and roasts to provide a savoury, rich flavour (see Table 11).

*Tempeh*, an Oriental fermented soya product is another source. It can be crumbled, pureed or deep fried and used in a similar way to *tofu* (see Table 10). Unfortunately, it is not yet widely available in Britain. Naturally fermented *soya sauce* also contains vitamin $B_{12}$.

The vitamin $B_{12}$ found in miso, tempeh and soya sauce is produced by bacteria present during the fermentation process. The same bacteria are found commonly in soil, which could explain why vegetables grown in soil contaminated by such bacteria contain vitamin $B_{12}$.

The vitamin is also thought to be present in sprouted beans

48

and seeds, brewers yeast and fermented drinks such as wine, beer and cider.

Vitamin $B_{12}$ is produced by the bacteria in the human colon (large intestine), but because it can only be absorbed in the small intestine in the presence of the 'intrinsic factor' this source may be of little value to the body and will be excreted unused.

Some studies have shown that people who have been vegan from birth *can* absorb the vitamin $B_{12}$ from their colon. This may be because the $B_{12}$ producing bacteria have colonised the small intestine. These studies have led to the theory that meat eating in childhood interferes with the body's natural ability to absorb vitamin $B_{12}$ from the colon.

Interestingly, omnivores are just as likely to suffer from vitamin $B_{12}$ deficiencies as vegans. This suggests that deficiency is more likely to be caused by the lack of ability to absorb the vitamin rather than a dietary deficiency.

VEGAN SOURCES

As studies have shown that the body stores enough vitamin $B_{12}$ to last 3–4 years and bearing in mind that $B_{12}$ producing bacteria are found in an enormous range of vegetable foods, it is highly unlikely that vegans will be deficient in the vitamin.

However, babies breast fed by vegan mothers and some vegan ethnic minority groups may be deficient in vitamin $B_{12}$. Until more is known about the absorption of the vitamin it is generally recommended that they either supplement or ensure that their diet contains fortified foods.

*Plamil* soya milk, various vegan convenience foods and some yeast extracts are fortified with vitamin $B_{12}$ produced from bacterial cultures and these are the best dietary sources. One teaspoonful (5 g) of fortified yeast extract daily will supply the required amount of vitamin $B_{12}$.

Other useful supplements are miso, kelp powder (made from seaweed), alfalfa sprouts, beer and cider.

# Minerals

Minerals, like vitamins, are substances required in minute quantities by the body to maintain health. Without the correct balance of each mineral in the body, basic bodily functions may be seriously impaired.

There are more than 90 minerals and it is highly probable that all of these are present in the human body, although most are in quantities that are too small to be detected.

## Classification

Twenty minerals are found in fairly large quantities in the body and these are known to be essential to health; six of these are present in large amounts and are called the major minerals — they are sodium, potassium, calcium, phosphorus, magnesium and chlorine.

The rest are present in smaller amounts and are called the trace elements — these include iron, copper, zinc, iodine and fluorine, the functions of which are well-documented. Iron is probably the most important.

The way in which the body uses the other trace elements is not yet fully understood — they are *chromium*, *cobalt*, *manganese*, *tin*, *vanadium*, *nickel*, *selenium*, *silicon* and *molybdenum*.

## Functions of minerals

Minerals all have specific functions in the body and usually work in conjunction with each other or with vitamins.

They are major components of blood, bones, teeth, nerve cells, body fluids and muscle fibres; are essential for the activation of enzymes and hormones, and assist the release of energy from food.

## Absorption

Unlike some vitamins, minerals cannot be made in the body so they must be obtained from food. The amount of minerals absorbed by the body normally balances the amount lost daily in sweat, urine and faeces.

Under certain conditions, for example during pregnancy or lactation and after an illness or in growing children, the body will require more minerals to assist in growth and repair.

As most minerals are concentrated in the outer leaves or skins of fruits and vegetables and are leached out in water, foods should be eaten whole and not peeled and any cooking liquid used for stock to maximise the mineral content of the diet.

### Enemies of minerals

Excessive doses of minerals upset and impair the delicate balance within the body and may be toxic. Dietary supplements should therefore only be taken if prescribed by a doctor, and, in a well-balanced vegan diet, should be unnecessary.

As many minerals are interdependent and present in foods in balanced quantities, the refining of food, addition of additives to processed foods and some drugs will reduce the minerals available for absorption by destroying one or more mineral so that the remaining ones cannot function. The use of mineral fertilizers in agriculture and excessive use of table salt will also upset the balance of minerals already present in the body.

### Vegans and minerals

As all the minerals are found in a wide range of plant foods, it is extremely unlikely that vegans will be deficient.

There is some concern about the intake of calcium and iron in the vegan diet because these two minerals are traditionally obtained from dairy foods and meat respectively, however, vegans can easily obtain their dietary requirements for both these minerals.

Table 3 summarizes the best vegan sources of the essential minerals; describes briefly how they are used by the body, and lists the deficiency symptoms for reference.

### Calcium

The recommended daily requirement of calcium is 500 mg; growing children require 600–700 mg and pregnant and lactating women who need more for growth, the formation of bones in the fetus and for breast milk require 1200 mg.

Calcium is the most abundant mineral in the body and in conjunction with phosphorus and magnesium is the most important biologically, binding with phosphorus to form calcium phosphate and magnesium phosphate which, in a process regulated by vitamin D, are laid down in the bones and teeth.

Phosphorus is used in a 1:2 ratio with calcium to form calcium phosphate. Therefore if the diet is too high in

51

**Table 3.** Summary of the major minerals and trace elements. RDI, recommended daily intake.

| RDI | Function in the body | Deficiency symptoms | Vegan sources |
|---|---|---|---|
| *Major minerals*<br>Sodium (Na) 4 g* | Binds to *chlorine* to form salt — an essential component of all body fluids circulating *outside* cells, the blood, and hydrochloric acid in the stomach. Works in conjunction with *potassium* maintaining water and acid/alkali balance of body; nerve and muscle activity; functioning of cell enzymes. Balance of sodium, potassium and chlorine is essential. Sodium is not needed from salt — natural foods have enough. Excess more common. Rapidly absorbed from food and excess is excreted in urine. Lost in sweat so intakes greater in hot climates or after strenuous exercise. | Deficiency causes muscular cramps and body dehydration. Excess causes fluid retention, damages kidneys and increases blood pressure. | *Occurs naturally* in green vegetables, carrots, alfalfa sprouts, lentils, dried fruit. *Added as salt to* bread, yeast extract, soy sauce, miso, pickles, margarine, stock cubes and most tinned foods. |
| Potassium (K) 3 g | Essential component of body fluid *inside* cells, muscle cells and blood. Works in conjunction with *sodium*. Balance of sodium and potassium vital — with excess sodium in relation to potassium, potassium will be excreted even if the body is deficient. Absorbed rapidly from food; excess excreted in urine. Losses are greater after diarrhoea and excessive use of laxatives or diuretics. Absorption reduced if diet is high in sugar, alcohol or coffee. | Weak muscles, mental confusion, poor reflexes, constipation, nervous disorders, swollen abdomen and dry skin. If severe, deficiency may result in a heart attack due to failure of heart muscles. Deficiency in vegans extremely unlikely. | Soya flour, tofu, beans, nuts, dried fruit, fresh fruit, fruit juices, bread, beansprouts, green vegetables, root vegetables, yeast extract, wholemeal flour. |

| Mineral | Function | Deficiency | Sources |
|---|---|---|---|
| Chlorine (Cl) 1 g* | Binds to *Sodium* to form salt (*sodium chloride*) which is present in body fluids, gastric juices and blood. Helps the liver function properly. Balance of Sodium and Chlorine essential. | As for sodium. | *Occurs naturally* in seaweed, kelp and olives. *Added as salt to* bread, yeast extract, margarine, miso, soy sauce, stock cubes, pickles and most canned foods. May be present in tap water. |
| Magnesium (Mg) 300 mg | Works in conjunction with *calcium* and to some extent *phosphorus* as a component of bones. Present in body tissues for functioning of enzymes. Essential to nerve functioning; acid/alkali balance of body; production of energy; metabolism of calcium and vitamin C. Health of bones, teeth, nerves, heart and muscles. Balance of calcium and magnesium is essential. Losses increase after diarrhoea, illness and use of laxatives and diuretics. Absorption reduced in the presence of *phytic acid* found in outer layers of grains. | Apathy, depression, muscle weakness, nervous disorders. If severe, leads to muscular spasms and possibly heart attacks. | Found in all plants as it is a component of the green pigment *chlorophyll*. Good sources are: nuts, soya flour, tofu, beans, wholemeal flour, lentils, dried and fresh fruits, alfalfa sprouts, yeast extract. |
| Phosphorus (P) 1.5 g | Second most abundant mineral in the body. Combines with *calcium* to form calcium phosphate — major component of bones and teeth. Other phosphates are active in the body — present in blood and tissues; helping to maintain acid/alkali balance of | Deficiency causes bone weakening as phosphorus is drawn out of the bones to be used elsewhere in the body. Deficiencies extremely unlikely in vegans as phosphorus is found in such an abundance of plant foods. | Yeast extract, nuts, wholemeal flour, beans, bread, lentils, dried fruit, green vegetables, cereals, mushrooms, root vegetables, beansprouts. |

**Table 3.** (contd)

| RDI | Function in the body | Deficiency symptoms | Vegan sources |
|---|---|---|---|
| | body; as components of cells; liberating energy from food; as components of some fats and for the correct functioning of the nervous system and the kidneys. Phosphorus also helps to utilise B-group vitamins in the body; necessary for healthy heart muscles and brain. | Excess upsets the calcium/phosphorus balance causing the body to be deficient in calcium. | |
| Calcium (Ca)† 500 mg | Most abundant mineral in the body. Works in conjunction with *magnesium, phosphorus* and *vitamin D* to form bones and teeth. Needs adequate supplies of vitamin D to be absorbed. Balance of calcium, magnesium and phosphorus is essential. Also vital to nerve functioning, enzyme activity, muscle contraction and, in conjunction with *vitamin K*, is needed for clotting of blood and healing of wounds. Health of skin, soft tissues, blood and heart. Absorption reduced in presence of *phytic acid (cereals)* and *oxalic acid (rhubarb and spinach)*. Excreted in urine and faeces. Losses increased in high protein and saturated fat/low in vitamin D diet. Some lost in sweat. | Deficiency causes muscle cramps and nervous spasms. If severe and there is also a deficiency of vitamin D, *rickets* may result in children. May cause bone softening (*osteomalacia*) in adults especially women who have repeated pregnancies and decalcification of bones (*osteoporosis*) in old people. These diseases are more likely to be caused by a deficiency of vitamin D so that too little calcium is absorbed rather than a lack of calcium in the diet. | Dried fruits, nuts, soya flour, tofu, soya milk, beansprouts, pulses, seeds, grains, bread, green vegetables, root vegetables. |

| | | | |
|---|---|---|---|
| *Trace elements*<br>Iron (Fe)†<br>10–12 mg | Important trace element. Over half body's iron used for formation of *haemoglobin*, (the red pigment in blood) and the production of enzymes used in respiration. *Copper-containing enzymes* are also necessary for the production of haemoglobin — balance of iron and copper is essential. Present in the muscle protein *myoglobin* and some is stored in the liver. Necessary for the proper metabolism of B-group vitamins; providing resistance to disease; healthy skin, hair, nails and bones. Poorly absorbed from plant sources, helping to regulate intake as excess is poisonous. Absorption is increased in the presence of Vitamin D, Copper, Cobalt and Manganese; when the liver's supply is depleted and when the body requirements are higher, e.g. in menstruating and pregnant women. | Deficiency causes general fatigue and lower resistance to disease (often thought to be emotional problems rather than iron deficiency). If severe, anaemia or angina may result. | Yeast extract, lentils, beans, dried fruit, wholemeal flour, bread, nuts, cereals, green vegetables, beansprouts. |
| Copper (Cu)<br>2–3 mg | Needed with *iron* for haemoglobin formation. Associated with several different enzymes; involved in the production of energy in muscles and pigment *melanin* which colours the skin and hair. Essential for the | Deficiency causes a loss of hair colour and sense of taste; raised blood cholesterol; fatigue; and anaemia. If serious — brain damage and seizures may result. Babies may suffer diarrhoea, | Beans, nuts, cereals, green vegetables, mushrooms, lentils, wholemeal flour, dried fruit, bread, yeast extract, cocoa. |

**Table 3.** (contd)

| RDI | Function in the body | Deficiency symptoms | Vegan sources |
|---|---|---|---|
| | utilisation of vitamin C. Health of bones, hair, blood, skin and circulation. Must bind to certain *amino-acids* found in protein for absorption which is inhibited by excess zinc, fluorine and molybdenum. Not properly absorbed during illness or while taking the pill or certain drugs. | stunted growth and anaemia so it vital for pregnant women to include adequate copper in the diet. Baby boys suffer *Menke's Syndrome* (hair to be stiff and colourless) if the mother was deficient in copper. Excess copper is extremely poisonous; leads to heart attacks, high blood pressure, cirrhosis of the liver and *Parkinson's disease. Wilson's disease* occurs when the body is unable to excrete copper and is deposited in the brain causing mental illness. Smoking and high oestrogen contraceptive pills increase levels of copper in the body. | |
| Iodine (I) 70–100 µg | Used by the thyroid gland to produce the *thyroxine* which is essential to regulate metabolism. Also needed for healthy hair, skin, nails and proper growth. Substances called *goitrogens* found in some green vegetables, reduce the absorption of iodine but these are largely removed during cooking. | Deficiency leads to mental and physical sluggishness, low vitality, poor circulation, reduction in metabolic rate, weight gain, dry skin and hair, and reduced blood pressure. If severe — the thyroid gland enlarges causing the condition *goitre*. Babies deficient in iodine may have abnormal | Green vegetables, sea salt, cereals, seaweed, kelp, onions. |

| Mineral | Function | Deficiency/Excess | Sources |
|---|---|---|---|
| | | brain development leading to *cretinism* or *deaf Mutism* so pregnant women should ensure a good intake in the diet. Iodine is extremely toxic in large doses. | |
| Fluorine (F) No RDI | Present in bones and teeth and is thought to increase hardening of tooth enamel that prevents decay. | Deficiency causes tooth decay but is extremely unlikely. Excess causes mottling and discolouration of the teeth and if taken in large doses is highly poisonous, causing the bones to become rigid and inflexible. Excess fluorine is also thought to be linked to some cancers. | Tap water, beverages made from water (especially tea), vegetables. |
| Zinc (Zn) 12–15 mg | Known as the protective mineral. Present in bones, tissues, muscles, hair, skin, nails and mucous membranes. Needed for the manufacture of protein; growth and cell reproduction; sexual development and fertility. Maintains acid/alkali balance of body fluid; activates some enzymes; helps healing of wounds. Helps in metabolism of carbohydrate, vitamin $B_1$, phosphorus and protein. Essential for functioning of prostate gland and brain and the release of the | Deficiency leads to stunted growth, white spots on the nails, loss of taste, loss of appetite, poor hair growth, rough skin, lack of sexual development and poor healing of wounds. Zinc is very important during pregnancy as deficiency can lead to abnormal babies. | Found in a wide variety of foods especially nuts, wholemeal flour, lentils, beans, bread, grains, root vegetables. |

**Table 3.** *(contd)*

| RDI | Function in the body | Deficiency symptoms | Vegan sources |
|-----|---------------------|---------------------|---------------|
| | hormone *insulin* from the pancreas. Zinc is used successfully in the treatment of acne. The absorption of zinc is reduced in the presence of *phytic acid* (cereals) and dietary fibre which binds to zinc and causes it to be excreted. It is also lost in sweat. A good intake should therefore be ensured. Alcohol and the pill lower zinc levels in the body. | | |
| Chromium (Cr) No RDI | Associated with the release of the hormone insulin from the pancreas which metabolises sugar in the body. Chromium is often linked to diabetes because of this relationship with insulin — diabetics have very low chromium levels in their bodies. Chromium is also used in the manufacture of fatty-acids, cholesterol and protein in the body. It is necessary for normal growth and may prevent high blood pressure and heart disease. Chromium is poorly | Deficiency of chromium leads to a rise in blood cholesterol but there are no clear deficiency symptoms as diabetes and heart disease may be caused by a number of other factors. | Brewers yeast, corn oil, grains, grape juice, bread, mushrooms, molasses, raw sugar. (Note: refined foods and white sugar are very low in chromium). |

absorbed and excreted in urine. It is a waste product of many industrial plants and if breathed in, may collect in the lungs.

| | | | |
|---|---|---|---|
| Cobalt (Co)‡ 1–3 µg | Cobalt is part of the structure of the Vitamin $B_{12}$ molecule and it utilised in this form. The cobalt in food *is not made into vitamin $B_{12}$ by the body* but as some is absorbed from food it is probably needed for other functions which have not yet been identified. There is a connection between cobalt and the thyroid gland hormones. It is not possible to get an overdose of cobalt from food. | Deficiency symptoms are not known other than the serious symptoms of Vitamin $B_{12}$ deficiency. Excess cobalt causes an enlargement of the thyroid gland known as goitre which normally only occurs if iodine is deficient. | If there is adequate vitamin $B_{12}$ in the diet, the cobalt will be adequate. |
| Tin (Sn) No RDI | Thought to be necessary for the manufacture of protein in the body. If tinned foods are exposed to air or have a high acid content, excess Tin may be leached out of the can into the food which can be harmful. Tinned foods should therefore be tipped out into a bowl when opened rather than being stored in the can. | Not known | Tin is found in foods which have been canned or wrapped in foil. Natural sources are not yet known. |

**Table 3.** (contd)

| RDI | Function in the body | Deficiency symptoms | Vegan sources |
|---|---|---|---|
| Selenium (Se)<br>No RDI | Works in conjunction with *vitamin E* as an antioxidant to prevent the destruction of cells by oxygen, the consequent hardening of tissue and premature ageing. Selenium is part of an enzyme system that controls prostaglandins (hormone-like substances) that regulate body functions. It also plays a part in reproduction — male semen contains a lot of selenium and it is found in the testicles and seminal glands. It appears to be necessary for the correct functioning of the pancreas and may relieve high blood pressure and the pain of angina. It also prevents dandruff. There is some controversial evidence to suggest that selenium may prevent breast and digestive tract cancers. | Deficiency is thought to contribute to heart, kidney and liver failure. The only conclusive deficiency symptom is acute dandruff. Extremely toxic if taken in large doses. | Wholegrains, wholemeal flour, bread, seaweed, rice. |
| Manganese (Mn)<br>4–7 mg | Acts as an enzyme activator in cells. Necessary for the metabolism of fats, carbohydrates, vitamins $B_1$, E, C and Biotin. Aids growth and skeletal | Deficiency is thought to interfere with sugar metabolism as diabetics are usually low in Manganese. No clear deficiency symptoms but | Wholegrains, nuts, leafy vegetables, spices, tea, bananas, celery, pulses, pineapple. |

| | | | |
|---|---|---|---|
| | development. Needed for the formation of thyroid gland hormones, sex hormones, normal reproduction and normal nerve functioning. Thought to be necessary for successful childbearing; building of genetic material in cells; the formation of babies in the womb; healthy brain, mammary glands and muscles. Manganese prevents excess copper building up in the body which is toxic. | weight loss, nausea and dermatitis have all been associated with a deficiency. | |
| Nickel (Ni) No RDI | Present in human tissues and may be essential for growth. Possibly needed for the health of the liver. | No clear deficiency symptoms but persons suffering heart attacks have been found to have abnormally high levels of nickel in their blood. | Found in margarine as nickel is part of the hydrogenation process used to solidify oils. May also dissolve from saucepans into food. |
| Molybdenum (Mo) No RDI | Present in enzyme systems used in the utilisation of iron from food — so prevents anaemia. Also necessary for carbohydrate and fat metabolism. Possibly an anti-tooth decay agent. Destroyed if the body contains excess copper. | No clear deficiency symptoms but excess causes a high production of uric acid that leads to gout, uric stones in the bladder and urinary passage and an increased risk of heart disease. | Green vegetables, pulses, grains. |
| Vanadium (V) No RDI | Needed for growth, reproduction, the metabolism of fats and cholesterol in blood. Slows down the body's production of cholesterol and inhibits its deposit in blood vessels. | No clear deficiency symptoms identified. | Nuts, root vegetables, grains. |

**Table 3.** (contd)

| RDI | Function in the body | Deficiency symptoms | Vegan sources |
|---|---|---|---|
| Silicon (Si)<br>No RDI | Silicon is present in the connective tissues between joints and organs. It may have a role to play in bone formation in conjunction with calcium. Silicon is a common food additive. It is also a pollutant found in some mines and quarries. If inhaled in excess it may cause silicosis which can be fatal. | No clear deficiency symptoms but may cause stunted growth and abnormal bone formation. | Wholegrains. |

* Intake generally higher. † More for children, and pregnant and lactating women. ‡ As for vitamin B$_{12}$.

References: Brown, S. *Healthy Living Cookbook* (Dorling Kindersley, 1985); Lucas J.W. *Vegetarian Nutrition* (The Vegetarian Society, 1979); Ministry of Agriculture, Fisheries and Food. *Manual of Nutrition* (HMSO, 1976); Polunin, M. *Minerals* (Thorsons Publishers Ltd., 1979); Saunders T.A.B. & Ellis, F.R. *Vegan Nutrition* (The Vegan Society, 1981).

phosphorus more calcium is required. Meat is particularly high in phosphorus so omnivores consuming a lot of meat may require more calcium in their diet than vegans.

In addition to the formation of bones, which account for virtually all the calcium present in the body, some calcium is required for other essential functions.

Calcium in conjunction with vitamin K is essential for blood clotting and healing of wounds. It is also needed for the contraction of muscles (including the heart), nerve functioning (especially in the eyes) and enzyme activity.

Calcium in bones is used as a reserve supply for any of the above functions and is constantly being drawn out of bones into the blood and then replaced in a carefully controlled process which is again regulated by vitamin D.

## ABSORPTION

Only about 25% of the calcium consumed in food will actually be absorbed by the body. The remainder will be lost in faeces, urine and, to a lesser extent, sweat. Adults normally absorb enough to balance these losses but absorption is considerably reduced if the diet is too high in protein or saturated fats, too low in Vitamin D or if there are large amounts of phytic or oxalic acid present.

*Phytic acid* is present in the outer layers (bran) of many grains, especially wheat. It is partly destroyed on cooking and during digestion so its presence in the diet is unlikely to be serious. However, sprinkling bran onto food that is to be eaten raw such as breakfast cereal, may significantly reduce the absoprtion of calcium.

*Oxalic acid* is present in fairly large amounts in rhubarb and spinach and, to a lesser extent, in tea, cocoa and beetroot. As none of these foods is likely to be eaten regularly in large amounts this too, is unlikely to cause problems.

Calcium is excreted from the body more rapidly if you are not taking much exercise. People who lead a sedentary lifestyle or are bedridden would therefore be advised to consume more calcium-rich foods.

Studies have shown that the body can adapt to lower calcium intakes by gradually reducing the amounts that are excreted. The ability to do this however, appears to be reduced if the person has been on a very high calcium diet for several years. The older a person is, the less calcium he/she absorbs and as calcium deficiencies are particularly serious in the elderly, this should be borne in mind when planning meals.

Deficiency of calcium is serious and closely associated with deficiencies of vitamin D. Initial calcium deficiency symptoms are muscle cramps and nervous spasms. Diseases such as rickets in children, osteomalacia in pregnant women and osteoporosis in old people are more likely to be caused by a deficiency of vitamin D that leads to insufficient calcium being absorbed than a lack of calcium in the diet.

VEGAN SOURCES

Calcium is readily obtainable in a vegan diet. The richest sources are nuts, dried fruit, tofu, soya flour, pulses, beansprouts, seeds, grains, bread, green and root vegetables and soya milk.

## Iron

Iron is one of the most important trace elements. It is absorbed in the small intestines where it binds to protein and is transported into the liver. Once in the liver over half of it will be used, in conjunction with copper-containing enzymes, for the formation of *haemoglobin*, the red pigment in blood.

Haemoglobin transports oxygen from the lungs to the body cells where it is vital for the release of energy from food that is part of the respiratory cycle.

The remaining iron will be converted into enzymes (also required for respiration) and either converted into the muscle protein called *myoglobin* or stored in the liver.

Stored iron acts as a reserve supply in case of deficiency and is vital during the first 6 months of a baby's life prior to weaning because the iron content of milk is very low.

Iron is also essential for the correct metabolism of the B-complex vitamins, providing resistance to disease, and for healthy skin, nails and bones.

ABSORPTION

The liver is capable of re-utilising the iron from worn-out red blood cells to manufacture new ones so supplies from food are not essential to red blood cell formation. However, adequate intake is necessary for functions other than blood formation and if there has been bleeding or injuries where body cells are destroyed.

Iron from plant sources tends to be more poorly absorbed than that from meat but this may be advantageous in regulating the iron in the body because excess iron is extremely poisonous.

Iron absorption is increased in the presence of *vitamin C, cobalt, copper* and *manganese* if the liver's supply is depleted, and when the body's requirements are higher, for example in menstruating and pregnant women. Absorption is reduced in the presence of phytic acid found in the outer layers of grains.

The recommended daily intake of iron is 10–12 mg and this increases to 13–15 mg for growing children and 15 mg for pregnant or menstruating women.

Some authorities have suggested that these figures are too low for vegans in view of the fact that the iron from plants is less readily absorbed. However, many studies have shown that the iron intakes of vegans are considerably higher in general, than those of omnivores, so deficiencies are unlikely to occur.

DEFICIENCIES

Initial iron deficiency symptoms such as fatigue and lower resistance to infection are very likely to be passed off as emotional, rather than dietary problems. If allowed to continue, severe deficiencies will eventually lead to anaemia and possibly angina (a heart disorder caused by lack of oxygen in the heart muscle). Anaemia is best treated with iron tablets which contain a particularly well absorbed form of iron rather than increasing the iron content of the diet.

Anaemia may also be the result of a deficiency of either vitamin $B_{12}$ or folic acid as both are involved with haemoglobin production. It is therefore important to ascertain the cause of the anaemia before attempting any kind of cure.

Low iron intakes and iron deficiency anaemia tend to be common amongst Asian vegans in this country, especially pregnant women and children. This may be because the staple adult foods such as polished rice are low in iron. Babies tend to receive prolonged breastfeeding and late weaning onto foods which are also low in iron. Iron is added to chapati flour to bring it up to the same level as wheat flour but it does not seem to be very well absorbed.

### VEGAN SOURCES

Iron is readily obtainable in a well balanced vegan diet. The richest sources are: yeast extract, lentils, beans, dried fruit, flour, bread, nuts, grains, green vegetables and beansprouts.

Cocoa, molasses and parsley are extremely rich in iron but are rarely eaten in sufficient quantities to significantly increase iron intake, however, they provide a useful supplement to the foods listed above.

# 3

# BECOMING VEGAN

For most people the change to veganism comes as a gradual
progression from a lacto-vegetarian diet (one which contains
dairy produce but no meat, fish or their derivatives). With the
exception of dairy foods and their derivatives (lactose, whey
and casein from milk; albumen and lecithin from eggs*)
vegans eat much the same as lacto-vegetarians so the change
in diet is slightly easier.

For an omnivore, the change to vegan food will be more
difficult initially as most will find the thought of cooking
without meat, fish, eggs, milk, cheese and their derivatives
quite bewildering. The task is made even more difficult if you
are part of a family as the other members may not agree with
your views or want to give up their favourite foods.

I am not going to suggest that it is easy but you will find that
a lot of the dishes you are already cooking can be made vegan
simply by replacing the type of fat used (e.g. replacing the
butter in 'beans on toast' for vegan margarine); substituting
dairy produce for its vegan counterpart (e.g. using soya milk
in sauces and desserts instead of cows milk); or omitting the
meat (e.g. making bean and vegetable casserole instead of
meat and vegetable casserole).

I hope that the following advice will help you to start
making the change.

---

* Lecithin may be obtained from either eggs or soya beans – so check first as it may be
vegan

## Where to Start

If you are an omnivore, I would strongly recommend you to spend about 6 months gradually reducing the amount of meat and fish meals in your diet and introducing more vegetarian and vegan meals before trying to become completely vegan. This will allow your body to adapt to the increased consumption of raw vegetables and wholefoods which may not have been included in the diet previously, and reduce the shock for the family!

Try to replace flesh foods with dishes made from nuts, grains, pulses and vegetables starting with nut and grain dishes before introducing pulses. Nuts and grains are more familiar and popular with children than pulses which have a taste and texture that may take a bit of getting used to and take longer to cook. Roasts, casseroles, pies, burgers and shepherd's pie all seem to be very popular with my non-vegetarian guests so these would be good dishes to start with. The sample menu (Table 4) gives you some ideas for quick and easy meals throughout the week. The lunch and dinner menus are interchangeable and the lunchtime suggestions could also be used for quick snacks or supper dishes if preferred. The dinner suggestions have all been chosen because they are similar in appearance to dishes that you will be used to already — this is very important when first introducing new dishes to children.

Initially you will have to be a bit more organised and long-sighted than usual and be prepared to spend more time in the kitchen cooking than before. Once you are familiar with foods and cooking methods however, vegan food takes no longer to prepare than other food.

If you are fortunate enough to own a food processor and a pressure cooker even more time can be saved. Food processors chop, grate, slice and purée vegetables in seconds to use in cooked dishes, salads, soups or sauces. They are also excellent for grinding nuts, making breadcrumbs, pastry, bread, cakes, biscuits and many other things. Pressure cookers are useful for steaming vegetables, reducing the cooking time of stews and casseroles and cooking dried pulses.

Vegan food freezes well, so if you have a freezer you can save time by batch baking when time allows.

If you are at first worried about cooking new dishes or don't

**Table 4.** Menu samples

| Breakfast | Lunch | Dinner |
| --- | --- | --- |
| *Monday*<br>Fruit juice; Muesli with soya milk; Toast with vegan margarine and jam; Tea/Coffee | Cold nutroast and cucumber sandwiches; Fruit cake; Piece of fruit | Lentil Shepherds Pie (p. 159); Salad; Fruit crumble (p. 251); Soya custard (p. 291) |
| *Tuesday*<br>½ grapefruit; Beans on toast; Tea/Coffee | Vegetable soup with roll; Muesli bar; Piece of fruit | Stir fry vegetables with rice and almonds (p. 222); Apricot slice (p. 273); Vanilla soya dessert |
| *Wednesday*<br>Fresh fruit; Cereal with soya milk or soya yogurt; Toast with vegan margarine and yeast extract; Tea/Coffee | Mixed salad with nuts; Jacket potato; Piece of fruit | Vegetable and barley stew with coriander (p. 198); Wholemeal bread; Cabbage; Hazelnut Eve Pudding (p. 253); Vegan icecream or soya dessert |

**Thursday**
Fruit juice; Bubble and squeak (with left over vegetables from Wed.); Toast with vegan margarine; Tea/Coffee

Lentil and Walnut pâté sandwich (p. 229); Soya yogurt; Piece of fruit

Pasta and vegetable savoury (p. 189); Salad; Fruit pie (p. 250); Nutcream (p. 289)

**Friday**
Stewed prunes; Muesli with soya milk; Wholemeal muffins with marmalade; Tea/Coffee

Peanut butter sandwich; Bean soup; Piece of fruit

Millet burgers (p. 170); Tomato sauce (p. 239); Jacket potato; Steamed vegetables; Apricot and banana whip (p. 278)

**Saturday**
½ grapefruit; Mushrooms on toast; Tea/Coffee

Millet burger left from last night in wholemeal bap with salad; Piece of fruit

Fruity cashew pilaff (p. 224); Salad; Apple and Sultana Charlotte (p. 252); Tofu cream (p. 290)

**Sunday**
Fresh fruit; Vegan packet-mix 'sausages' with beans and tomato; Muffins with jam; Tea/Coffee

Salad with smoked tofu cubes; Bread; Piece of fruit

Nutroast (p. 116); miso sauce (p. 240); Roast potatoes; Vegetables; Rice pudding (p. 259); Stewed dried fruit.

have time, most health food shops and supermarkets sell an ever-increasing range of time saving frozen, tinned or packeted convenience meals such as nutroast, burger/sausage mix, curries, casseroles, pasta dishes and pies as well as a range of tinned pulses. They can be used as they are or incorporated into a new dish — for example burger mix is a good base for a shepherd's pie and tinned vegetable casserole makes a tasty pie filling. Like all convenience products however, they are not as good as home-made!

Try to stick to wholefoods such as pulses, nuts, brown rice, wholemeal flour, wholemeal pasta etc. and eat as many raw salads as possible. This will ensure a well balanced diet with plenty of vitamins and minerals. Avoid foods containing animal fats (lard and suet), foods containing gelatine (made from animal hooves) and all highly processed foods containing additives, preservatives and colourings.

Unfortunately, a lot of processed foods are very popular with children; for example biscuits, cakes, dessert mixes and confectionary. However, there have been a lot of changes in recent years and most supermarkets now stock various biscuits and confectionary-type items made from vegetable fat and without additives. Vegan cakes and desserts are easily made at home by leaving out the eggs and using wholefood ingredients (see p. 75). If your children have confectionary, try giving them one of the many wholefood bars available in health food shops. Certain brands of chocolate and other sweets are vegan but as confectionary is not labelled with a list of ingredients in this country, it is very difficult to know whether it is suitable or not. The Vegan Society (see address list) produces an excellent Shoppers Guide which enables you to see at a glance which commonly found food products are acceptable to vegans.

Flavouring savoury dishes may seem like a problem at first when you are used to the taste of meat and dairy foods. Once your taste-buds have adapted to wholefoods and vegan 'dairy' foods (see p. 73) you will appreciate the more subtle, less highly seasoned flavours and textures of the plant kingdom, and cravings for salty, sugary foods will diminish. In order to help you flavour dishes and make them savoury and tasty I have listed a variety of flavourings (see Table 11). The most useful ones to have in the cupboard are vegetable stock cubes or paste, yeast extract and soy sauce. Herbs and spices (see Table 12) are another invaluable means of enhancing the flavour of dishes and most of my recipes contain a combination of both to give a really tasty flavour.

Meal planning will eventually become habit rather than chore and is made considerably easier if you have a stock of pulses, nuts, grains and vegan flavouring agents in the cupboard. Most wholefood shops have a fantastic array of pulses, nuts, grains and other products which can be quite confusing to the novice vegan attempting to stock up his/her store cupboard. There is nothing more disappointing than getting your unusual purchases home only to find you don't know how to cook them and consequently pushing them to the back of the cupboard where they may stay for years! To help you start, I have listed (Table 5) the basic ingredients that you will need to cook tasty vegan dishes such as those listed in the weekly menu plan (Table 4). Once you have these in the cupboard, you will only need to purchase fresh fruit and vegetables to make up meals. I find it helpful to buy lots of vegetables at the beginning of the week and then plan meals round these. Seeing what you have in the vegetable basket often provides inspiration!

**Table 5.**  Basic shopping list.

| | |
|---|---|
| Red and green lentils | Yeast extract |
| Wholemeal flour | Vegetable stock cubes |
| Hazelnuts | Soy sauce |
| Walnuts | Tomato purée |
| Brown rice | Peanut butter |
| (long and short grain) | |
| Millet | Muesli |
| Wholemeal pasta | Dried apricots |
| Vegetable oil | Sultanas |
| Vegan margarine | Sugar-free jam |
| Soya milk | Provamel vanilla soya dessert |
| Wholemeal bread | |
| Tinned kidney beans/chick peas | |

This may look like a daunting list but once you have these basics, you will find that your food bills are much lower (see p. 11).

Once you and the family are accustomed to vegetarian meals you can start introducing vegan 'dairy' foods.

## Vegan Alternatives

### Milk and milk products

Many life-long vegans do not use milk substitutes at all but for those who have been used to milk or feel they need it, there are numerous brands of soya milk available which can be used just like cows milk and have a similar nutritional value (Table 10). Soya milks are sold either in concentrated form which needs diluting (e.g. *Plamil*), ready to drink form (e.g. *Granose*) or powder form (e.g. *Boots* own brand). I personally prefer the concentrated form as it is more creamy but individual tastes vary. Most supermarkets and all health food stores stock a variety of brands and the best thing to do is try several until you find one you prefer. I would advise you to try a sweetened one to start with until you get used to the flavour and texture which is quite different from cows milk.

I cannot pretend that I liked soya milk the first time I tried it — I hated it! However, with perserverance I eventually found a brand I preferred and now enjoy its delicious nutty flavour on my breakfast every morning.

Soya milk can be used in cooking to make creamy sauces and desserts as well as on cereals and in drinks. Try rice pudding made with soya milk — deliciously creamy and rich (p. 259).

However, it is not terribly successful in hot drinks such as coffee as the acidity of the drink makes the milk curdle. The resulting drink may taste perfectly alright but looks far from appetising! One way round this is to allow the coffee to cool slightly before adding the milk. Strangely enough, tea does not seem to have the same effect on soya milk. I personally prefer my drinks black and many vegans do not drink tea and coffee anyway because of the caffeine content, preferring herbal teas which do not require milk.

Soya milk can be made into milkshakes with fresh fruit or fruit juice concentrates — a good way of disguising it for children. Some brands are available in flavoured form such as chocolate and strawberry which are also very popular.

Soya yoghurt is available in some health stores but at present only in limited flavours. It can be made at home from soya milk (the concentrated one gives a more creamy result) in a yoghurt maker or thermos flask using cows yoghurt or commercial starter as a setting agent. The first batch will obviously not be vegan but subsequent batches using the soya yoghurt as a starter, will be. Home-made soya yoghurt can have fresh fruit added to produce a delicious, healthy dessert or breakfast cereal topping.

Mums with young children will be pleased to hear that *Sunrise*, the soya milk manufacturers, now produce a vegan icecream which is absolutely delicious on its own or with desserts. Another vegan icecream called *Vive* is available in *Sainsburys* and some branches of *Co-op* although it does contain quite a lot of additives. You can make your own vegan icecream if you have a freezer — see recipes p. 275–76.

There are several vegan creams and dessert toppings available in health stores and some supermarkets. A soya cream called *Delice* is exclusive to health stores but *Sainsburys* make their own non-dairy cream which whips and can be used in cooking. Undiluted *Plamil* soya milk makes a good dessert topping as does a delicious soya dessert made by both *Provamel* and *Granose* in a variety of flavours. These are similar to blancmange and are ideal for children. Nutcreams can be made at home from ground almonds and cashews (see p. 289).

### Butter and cooking fat

Butter can be substituted for one of the various brands of vegan margarine now available e.g. *Granose*, *Hawthorn Vale*, *Suma*, *Vitaquel*, *Tomor*. Vegan margarine differs from ordinary margarine only in that it contains no whey. It cooks, tastes and spreads exactly like other brands. *Granose* is now being sold in some branches of *Waitrose* which makes it considerably cheaper.

There are numerous white vegetable fats available to use in place of lard e.g. *White Flora*, *Trex*, *Nutter*, *Suenut*. These are ideal for pastries and frying but are highly saturated (see p. 24) so it may be better to stick to a polyunsaturated oil for frying. Vegetable suet called *Broadland* is now available as a convenient alternative to beef suet in steamed puddings and suet-crust pastry.

### Cheese

There are no commercially available vegan cheeses on the

market, but tofu (soya bean curd) is a versatile 'cheese-like' product with an excellent nutritive value that can be used in sweet and savoury dishes (see p. 100–101). It is very bland and therefore needs careful flavouring to make it palatable although a smoked variety is available which is absolutely delicious and can be cubed in salads. Try tofu burgers (p. 169), tofu quiche (p. 149) and tofu cheesecake (p. 281).

The other way to make a vegan 'cheese' is to melt some hard margarine (e.g. *Tomor*) and stir in an equal quantity of soya flour. Flavour it with yeast extract, soy sauce, herbs etc. then chill it and allow to harden. It can be cubed or sliced to serve in salads or sandwiches.

Alternatively, nutritional yeast flakes or powder taste very 'cheesy' when added to spreads, sauces and toppings. They are expensive however and quite difficult to find — do not confuse with brewers yeast which is a different strain of yeast.


### Gelatine

Gelatine is made from animal hooves and is therefore not acceptable to vegans. *Agar agar* is a vegan gelling agent made from seaweed which is available in powder form. It can be used like gelatine to make jellies and set mousses, fools and desserts (see pp. 277–281). Vegan jelly crystals and mixes can be found in most health food shops (e.g. *Gelozone*, *Snow Crest*, *Mr. Merry*) and some commercial jellies are vegan e.g. *Chivers*. *The Vegan Shoppers Guide* gives more details.


### Eggs

Eggs are not necessary for cakemaking, batters or binding as there are numerous vegan substitutes. Mashed tofu mixed with soy sauce, herbs and pepper makes a good substitute for scrambled egg and is just as nutritious.

Eggless cakes and sponge toppings can be made easily by adding extra liquid (usually oil) and increasing the amount of raising agent used (baking powder) — see recipes p. 253–256.

Agar agar or tofu can be used to set cheesecakes, mousses or fools and batters can be made from soya flour, chickpea (gram or besan) flour, wheat flour, oil and soya milk — see recipe p. 179.

Vegetable stock is a good binder for burgers and roasts, as

is a thick white sauce made with soya milk (see recipes p. 118, 125). If you have a favourite recipe that uses egg to bind try the following substitutes:

1 egg = 4 oz (100 g) silken tofu blended with water
*or* 1 tablespoon chick pea/soya flour plus 1 tablespoon water
These both supply protein, calcium, minerals and vitamins but are low in fat and cholesterol.

Soya lecithin also makes a good egg substitute for binding — reconstitute according to instructions on packet.

Hopefully after reading this you will realise that it is not as difficult to be vegan as you may have first thought. Whatever you can cook in a 'normal' diet you can make vegan just by substituting one or two ingredients for their vegan counterparts.

## Cooking for One

If you live alone, becoming vegan is even easier as you do not have to worry about cooking for anyone else! Nuts, pulses and grains keep for several months provided they are kept in cool, airtight containers. This avoids the necessity of continually buying small quantities of food just for one meal.

All the recipes in this book can be halved to provide a quantity that will serve two people so you can either eat it two days running, or turn it into something else the following day to provide variety (Table 6). Vegan food is extremely versatile and will easily double up as something completely different to ring the changes.

If you are lucky enough to have a small freezer you could eat something different every night by cooking a full quantity of any dish and freezing it in four individual portions.

## Away from Home

Recent years have seen a massive growth in the demand for vegetarian meals and it is now quite rare to find a town that does not have at least one health food shop, vegetarian restaurant or restaurant that serves vegetarian meals. The choice for vegans may still be limited though so it is advisable to ring and check in advance. Be explicit and list the foods you do and do not eat — this will avoid the disappointment of

**Table 6.** Vegan food is very versatile.

| Day 1 | Day 2 |
| --- | --- |
| Nutroast | Make into burgers and fry or serve cold as a pâté. |
| Vegetable stew | Add some curry spices and serve with rice or use as a filling for a pasty. |
| Lentil bake | Top with potato and serve as shepherd's pie. |
| Risotto | Add some nuts or beans and use to stuff a pepper, courgette or marrow ring. |
| Pasta sauces | Serve with pasta one day and grain the next or add some cooked beans and make a crumble or a pasty. |

being served what would otherwise be a vegan meal apart from the butter on the vegetables or mayonnaise on the salad. Indian and Chinese restaurants usually provide vegan meals.

When travelling it is probably a good idea to take something to nibble although some airlines and most ships are quite good at providing vegan fare. Generally speaking, countries which have a Hindu or Buddhist religion can be relied on for vegan food but it is as well to book vegan meals in advance sending lists of foods eaten with sample recipes.


## Vegan Babies and Children

The vegan diet is not harmful to pregnant women, babies or children providing it is well balanced and has adequate vitamins $B_{12}$ and D (see p. 35, 47). Studies have shown pregnant vegan women to be more healthy and energetic than their non-vegan counterparts and generally have easier births and fewer complications.

Vegan babies and children have been shown to have an equal growth rate to their peers and are just as strong and fit. They tend to have lower levels of body fat (thereby reducing the risk of obesity), lower blood cholesterol, fewer allergies and less incidence of dental problems. There are many second generation vegans living healthy, happy lives today and medical opinion is gradually changing in their favour.

Not having had a child myself, I have no personal experience of pregnancy or rearing vegan babies but I have listed some very useful and comprehensive publications which may be of help to those wishing to start a family (p. 299). The Vegetarian and Vegan Societies both publish leaflets and provide information about local mother and toddler groups.

## What Else to Give Up

After changing your diet you may want to give up non-food items such as leather, wool, and silk and all products that contain animal ingredients or are tested on animals e.g. soap, cosmetics, detergents and toothpaste. Alternatives to all such products are becoming increasingly available and a list is available from the Vegan Society to help you choose.

Decisions to give up non-food items are usually made gradually as you begin to read more vegan literature and become aware of the inherent cruelty involved in the production of such goods. Some people may throw away all their shoes and toiletries immediately but it may not be possible for everyone to do this as the vegan alternatives may be more expensive or not easily obtainable.

Most fashion shoe shops sell plastic or canvas shoes and big stores such as *Marks and Spencer* or *British Home Stores* also stock a good range. Most fashion shops and chain stores sell acrylic knitwear, and vegan toiletries are widely available in health food shops and some chemists. *The Body Shop* range of products are not tested on animals but some contain lanolin (fat from sheeps wool) or milk, so check the labels first.

Everyone is free to choose what suits their lifestyle best but ideally all exploitative items will eventually be eliminated.

### The Vegan message

Vegan food is not a substitute for anything, nor is veganism a deprived or spartan way of life. It is delicious and nutritious food in its own right and the giving up of all animal products results in a truly compassionate, humane and unexploitative way of life.

# 4

# USING VEGAN FOODS

**Nuts**

Nuts are one of our most neglected foods (most people eat them only at Christmas!) but actually they provide the richest and most valuable source of vegan protein.

The most common varieties available are: hazels, walnuts, cashews, almonds and brazils. Peanuts, which are probably one of the most widely eaten nuts are not really nuts at all as they grow in pods underground like legumes (hence their other name — groundnuts). They have a similar appearance, texture and nutritional value to other nuts, and I will therefore group them together.

All nuts have their own characteristic flavour and texture but can generally be substituted for one another in recipes if particular varieties are not available at the time.

*Nutritional value*

Nuts are an excellent source of protein and are rich in sulphur-containing amino-acids which are not commonly found in the plant kingdom (especially Brazil nuts). Almonds and peanuts have the highest protein content, peanuts also being the highest vegetable source of vitamin $B_5$ (pantothenic acid). The protein value of nuts is increased when they are eaten with pulses.

Nuts have a high percentage of fat, a high proportion of which is polyunsaturated (the exception being coconut which is highly saturated). This means they have a high calorific value and are therefore one of the best energy-giving foods in a vegan diet.

Nuts contain vitamins A, B-group, folic acid, biotin and E, and mineral elements calcium, iron, magnesium, copper, zinc, potassium and phosphorus. They are also rich in dietary fibre.

### Uses in the diet

Nuts are the most expensive vegan food and hence tend to be used less frequently than other proteins such as grains and pulses.

Some nuts are pressed to produce oils e.g. peanut and almond but are generally eaten whole, chopped or ground in savoury dishes, salads and sweets.

To obtain maximum nutritive value, nuts should be eaten raw. This can easily be achieved by adding them to breakfast cereals, salads, cold sweets and by sprinkling onto cooked dishes.

However, nuts are also delicious cooked and for savoury dishes may be lightly roasted to enhance flavour. To do this, spread the nuts on a baking tray and roast for 5 minutes in a moderate oven (Gas 5/190 °C/375 °F) shaking regularly to prevent burning. The roasted nuts can then be chopped or ground as required.

Roasted or unroasted nuts can be used in a variety of savoury dishes, e.g. nut roast, nut rissoles, stuffings, bakes and crumble toppings or as an ingredient in baked sweets such as hazelnut eves pudding, bakewell tart, pastries, cakes and biscuits. They may also be used to make nut cream to serve with hot sweets and nut butters such as peanut butter.

### Storage

As nuts contain a high percentage of fat, they will go rancid when shelled if kept for long periods. Buy from a shop with a high turnover, store in cool, airtight containers and use within 3–4 months for maximum freshness. Nuts with shells left on will keep for up to 1 year.

### Seeds

Whole seeds, like nuts, are a very valuable source of protein in the vegan diet although they are more commonly pressed to produce oils which are a source of energy. The most common varities of seeds are sesame, sunflower and pumpkin which are used whole in savoury or sweet dishes.

Some seeds are sprouted for use in salads, e.g. alfalfa, cress and sesame. Many aromatic seeds are used whole or ground as a flavouring in spicy dishes, e.g. cumin, coriander, carraway, dill and fennel.

*Nutritional value*

Whole seeds are rich in protein, fat, B-vitamins and vitamin E, calcium, magnesium, phosphorus and fibre. If sprouted, the vitamin and mineral content of seeds increases considerably (see p. 101). Alfalfa sprouts are a source of the elusive vitamin $B_{12}$.

Oils made from seeds (e.g. sunflower, safflower) are the most important source of energy in a vegan diet, either in the form of liquid cooking oils, solid vegetable fat or vegan margarines. They are highly polyunsaturated and if cold pressed and unrefined (see p. 28) are also an excellent source of minerals.

Sesame seeds may be crushed to a paste called *tahini* which is rich in fat and calcium.

*Uses in the diet*

Seeds can be roasted in the oven in the same way as nuts or may be dry roasted in a frying pan on a low heat to achieve the same results.

Roasted sunflower seeds sprinkled with tamari (soy) sauce make a delicious, nutritious snack.

Whole seeds can be ground and used in bakes, pâtés and roasts or used as they are in crumble toppings, breakfast cereals, salads, cakes and biscuits.

Tahini makes a lovely sandwich spread (like peanut butter) or an ingredient for dips and pâtés. It is also an excellent thickening agent for casseroles and stews. Banana dipped in tahini makes a delicious snack.

Seed sprouts may be eaten raw in salads and sandwiches or stir-fried to add crunchy texture to vegetables or rice dishes.

**Table 7.** Storage of seeds and seed products.

| | |
|---|---|
| Whole seeds | Store in cool, airtight containers and use within 6 months for maximum freshness. |
| Seed sprouts | Keep 3–4 days in fridge. |
| Tahini | Keeps approx. 6 months unrefrigerated. |
| Unrefined oils | Store in a cool place, preferably in dark bottles. Use within 6 months. |
| Margarines and solid vegetable fats | Keeps for several months if refrigerated. |

## Grains (cereals)

Grains, also known as cereals, are an excellent source of protein in the vegan diet, particularly when they are combined with pulses which increase the biological value (see p. 21) of the protein.

They also provide carbohydrate, vitamins, minerals and fibre and are relatively cheap when compared with other protein foods e.g. nuts. Grains are low in fat but are very filling, and are therefore useful in slimming diets.

The main grains used in this country are wheat, rice, millet, oats, maize, barley and rye. Buckwheat is usually classed as a grain although in actual fact it is a seed.

Grains can be eaten whole, ground into flour, flaked or pre-cooked and then cracked for quick cooking. Whole grains soak up a lot of liquid during cooking and swell to 2–3 times their original bulk. When grains are to be eaten whole, a general serving guide is to allow 2–3 oz. (50–75 g) dry grain per person. All grains should be washed prior to cooking to remove any dust or grit.

Grains and grain products have a long shelf-life provided they are kept in cool, airtight containers. They can therefore be bought in bulk more cheaply which makes them even more economical. Whenever possible it is better to buy organically grown grains which are free from pesticide and insecticide residues.

Different grains have their own characteristic flavour, texture, nutritional value, cooking times and uses in the diet (Table 8).

**Table 8.** Grains

| Product | Cooking | Uses in diet | Storage |
|---|---|---|---|
| *Wheat Flour.*<br>Milled grains of wheat. May be *100% wholemeal* (the whole grain); *81%* (15% of bran removed); *granary* (81% plus malted wheat grains); *white* (made from endosperm with bran and germ removed). 100% wholemeal has the best flavour, nutritional value and texture. | Wholemeal flour can be substituted for white in any recipe to give a better texture, flavour and nutritive value. | Use in bread, cakes, pastry, sauces, doughs, biscuits, batters. | Use within 6 months or fat in germ will go musty. |
| *Wheatbran*<br>Outer layer of wheat extracted during milling of flour. | | Add to breakfast cereals, crumble toppings, pastry, cakes, biscuits to increase fibre and vitamins. | Best used within 6 months. |
| *Wheatgerm*<br>Part of wheat grain that contains fats. Extracted during milling of flour. | | Health food in its own right. Used to produce oil — a rich source of vitamin E. Add to cereals, pastry, cakes, biscuits, crumble toppings. | *Unstabilised* Keeps 1 month in fridge. *Stabilised* Keeps 2–3 months unrefrigerated. |
| *Wheatflakes*<br>Whole wheat that has been crushed, rolled and cooked. | | Add to breakfast cereal, biscuits, dessert recipes. Use to coat burgers. | Keep 6–8 months. |

**Table 8.** (contd)

| Product | Cooking | Uses in diet | Storage |
|---|---|---|---|
| *Wheat Berries*<br>Whole grains of wheat. | Can be cooked and used like other grains. Cover with water/ stock and simmer, covered for 45–60 mins. until soft and grains begin to burst. Drain and serve. | Use like rice as a base for sauces; add to casseroles for more protein and texture; or use cold in salads for nutty, crunchy texture. Can be sprouted which increases nutritive value. | Keep 1 year but the older they are the longer they take to cook. |
| *Whole Wheat Pasta (dried)*<br>Dried and sold in variety of shapes, e.g. macaroni, shells, spaghetti, lasagne. | Add to boiling water with a drop of oil added and boil vigorously for 10–15 mins. depending on type of pasta. Drain and toss in oil or margarine. | Serve with sauces, add to casseroles and bakes or serve cold as salad ingredient. | Keeps 12 months. |
| *Bulgar Wheat*<br>Wheat which has been cracked, soaked and cooked to produce dried product that cooks very quickly. Yellowish colour. | Cover with boiling water/stock and allow to swell for 2–3 mins. Squeeze out excess water and use. | Serve hot like rice with sauces or cold as a base for salad. Use to bulk out burgers and roasts or stuff vegetables. | Keeps 12 months. |

| | | | |
|---|---|---|---|
| *Couscous*<br>Made in a similar way to bulgar from *semolina* (another wheat product). Creamy colour. | Soak in stock/water until swollen, drain and then steam gently for 30 mins. Stir in a knob of margarine and some pepper before serving.<br>*Alternatively*: cook in special cous cous steamer (couscoussier) or soak until swollen and steam in a pressure cooker for 3 mins. on high (15lb) pressure. Couscous may also be simmered in stock or water for 10–15 mins. but this breaks up the texture slightly. Bland flavour so benefits from being fried in oil/margarine before use. | Use as for bulgar. | Keeps 12 months. |
| *Whole Buckwheat*<br>The whole seed. Small, brown and pointed. Characteristic flavour. | Can be roasted to give a tasty flavour — put buckwheat in a dry or oiled frying pan on a low heat and stir for 5 mins. until browning. Then cover with water/stock and simmer covered for 20–30 mins. until soft. Drain and use. | Can be used as other grains. Used as a base for sauces, add to casseroles or serve cold in salads. | Keeps 12 months. |

**Table 8.** (*contd*)

| Product | Cooking | Uses in diet | Storage |
|---|---|---|---|
| *Buckwheat Flour*<br>Milled whole buckwheat. A dark speckled flour with very characteristic flavour. | | Can be added to other flours to improve nutritional value. Commonly used to make batter for savoury pancakes. May be added to pastry. | Use within 6 months. |
| *Buckwheat Pasta*<br>Made from buckwheat flour. Usually spaghetti and noodles. Popular in Far East especially Japan. | Add to boiling water with drop of oil added and boil vigorously for 3–5 mins. Drain and toss in oil or margarine. Delicate flavour. | Serve with sauces, add to casseroles or serve cold chopped up in salad. | Keeps 12 months. |
| *Whole Rice*<br>Has the outer indigestible husk removed to leave brown rice with an outer layer of bran. Brown rice varies with the country of origin — Thai brown rice is said to be the best quality. Can be either long grain (savoury) or short grain (sweet). | Takes longer to cook than white rice. Simmer, covered, in water/stock for 40–45 mins. Rinse in boiling water to separate grains. May also be baked in a low oven in stock (about 2 hours) or mixed into casseroles. | Use hot as a base for sauces or as a bulker in pies, roasts and rissoles. Use cold in salad. Short grain rice can be made into puddings with soya milk. | Keeps 12 months. |

| | | |
|---|---|---|
| *Puffed Rice* Rice which has been cooked and processed to give a light, crispy grain. | Used commercially in breakfast cereals and rice cakes. | Keeps 6 months. |
| *Rice Flour* Brown rice flour is low in gluten and therefore suitable for specialist diets. | Use as a shortener in biscuits, pastries, crumble toppings. Used as a thickener for soups, sauces and casseroles. | Use within 6 months. |
| *Whole Millet* A tiny round yellow seed used in Africa as a staple food. Can be cooked and used like other grains. | May be roasted like buckwheat before cooking to improve flavour. Simmer, covered in water/stock for 30–40 mins. until soft and swollen. Tends to go mushy and stick together but if slightly undercooked it can be rinsed in a seive to separate the grains. Excellent for burgers and roasts because of its mushy, binding texture. Can also be used like rice with sauces or added to casseroles. Has a fairly bland flavour so season well and use plenty of onions, garlic and herbs etc. | Keeps 12 months. |
| *Millet Flakes* Millet that has been crushed, rolled and cooked. | Can be added to pastry to improve nutritional value. Used in cereals, cakes, biscuits, crumble toppings and burger coating. | Use within 6 months. |

**Table 8.** (contd)

| Product | Cooking | Uses in diet | Storage |
|---|---|---|---|
| *Fresh Maize*<br>Fresh maize has plump juicy yellow kernels surrounded in a green papery husk that has a brown silky tip. | Remove the husk and the brown silk and rinse the cob in cold water. Boil or steam whole cobs for 3–5 mins. until tender and serve with margarine and black pepper. Alternatively remove the silk but not the husk and roast in a baking dish for 30 mins. Gas 4/180°C/350°F. (May also be roasted with husk removed if covered in foil). | As a vegetable, a starter before a main course or a barbecue item. | Store in fridge and eat as soon as possible within 3 days. |
| *Tinned/Frozen Maize*<br>Large amounts of corn are tinned or frozen after being removed from the cob. Pre-cooked. | Heat in a pan with a knob of margarine for 3 mins. until hot. Can be thawed/drained and eaten cold. | As a vegetable, an ingredient of casseroles etc. or cold in salads. | *Frozen* keeps 1 year in freezer. *Tinned* keeps indefinitely. |
| *Maize Flakes*<br>Kernels that have been crushed and cooked. | | Commonly known as cornflakes — used in cereals, biscuits, crumble toppings. | Keep 6–8 months. |

**Maize Meal**
Ground corn kernels. Cooked.
Bright yellow colour.

Used as a thickener in sauces
and casseroles. Also used to
make batters and breads.

Keeps 6 months.

**Maize Oil**
Made from pressed kernels.
Polyunsaturated. Deep golden
colour.

Used in margarine
manufacture. Good for all
frying, baking and salads.

*Unrefined* keeps 6 months.
*Refined* keeps 12 months or
longer.

**Rolled Oats**
The most common form in
which oats are sold. Flaked and
ready cooked.

Use in breakfast cereals,
porridge. Add to biscuits,
cakes, crumble toppings or use
to coat burgers.

Keep 6–8 months.

**Oatmeal**
Ground oats — available in
fine, medium or coarse
varieties.

Course oatmeal can be made
into a lovely thick porridge.
Soak overnight in water then
add soya milk to cover and
cook on a low heat for 30–40
mins. until thick and all the
milk is absorbed. Serve with
dried or fresh fruit.

Fine oatmeal is used as a
shortening agent in biscuits and
pastries. Medium and coarse
oatmeal can be added to bakes
and burgers (coarse oatmeal
needs soaking first in stock or
water). Medium oatmeal can
be used as a burger coating.

Use within 6 months.

**Whole Barley**
Pot barley has the outer
indigestible husk removed in a
similar way to rice. It is
nutritionally superior to pearl
barley which has the bran and
germ removed as well.

Simmer in stock/water for
40–60 mins. until grains are
soft and swollen. Can be rinsed
in a colander to separate the
grains.

Commonly used in stews and
casseroles but can also be eaten
like rice with sauces. Use as a
bulker in pies, bakes and
burgers.

Keeps 12 months.

**Table 8.** *(contd)*

| Product | Cooking | Uses in diet | Storage |
| --- | --- | --- | --- |
| *Barley Flour*<br>Very fine, pale coloured flour. | | Used with wheat flour in breads and cakes. Can also be used as a thickener like cornmeal in sauces. | Keeps 6 months. |
| *Barley Flakes*<br>Rolled barley that is processed and cooked. | | Add to breakfast cereals, cakes and biscuits. Use to coat burgers. | Keep 6 months. |
| *Whole Rye*<br>Not commonly found in shops. Can be used like rice. | Cook like barley or rice for 40–60 mins. until soft. | Use as whole rice or barley. | Keeps 12 months. |
| *Rye Flour*<br>May be dark or light depending on how much bran is removed. Has characteristic flavour. | | Most commonly used to make rye bread — close textured, dark and flat due to lack of gluten in rye. | Keeps 6 months. |
| *Rye Flakes*<br>Rolled grain — precooked. | | Add to muesli, biscuits and crumble toppings. Used to coat burgers. | Keeps 6 months. |

### Whole wheat

Whole wheat contains protein, carbohydrate, some fat, B-vitamins, folic acid and vitamin E, sodium, potassium, magnesium, calcium, phosphorus, iron, copper and zinc. The outer layer or 'bran' is a valuable source of fibre.

Whole wheat is the least digestible of all the grains and may cause allergies in certain people. See Table 8.

### Buckwheat

Buckwheat contains protein, carbohydrate, vitamins B-group and P, iron and fibre. It has a very high calcium content compared to other grains.

### Rice

Brown rice contains protein, carbohydrate, B-group vitamins, calcium, phosphorus, iron, copper, zinc and fibre. It is the world's largest food crop and is very popular because of its delicious nutty flavour, easy digestibility and low calorific value. It is not usually allergy forming so is useful for patients allergic to wheat. Low in gluten.

### Millet

Millet has the highest vitamin and mineral content of all the grains particularly iron, magnesium and B-group vitamins. It has a high protein content and contains carbohydrate, fat and fibre. It is easily digestible and contains no gluten so it is suitable for those allergic to wheat.

### Maize (corn)

Maize or corn is one of the most widely cultivated grains. it is rich in protein, fat, carbohydrate, B-group vitamins and E, phosphorus and fibre. Fresh corn also contains vitamins A and C.

### Oats

Oats have the highest protein and fat content of all the grains. They are also rich in iron, magnesium, calcium, potassium, phosphorus, sodium, copper, zinc, B-vitamins and folic acid. Like all grains, oats also contain carbohydrate and fibre.

### Barley

Barley is rich in protein, carbohydrates, fibre, B-vitamins and minerals. It is easily digestible and very filling which is why it is a traditional winter food. Low in gluten.

### Rye

Rye is rich in protein, carbohydrate, fat, potassium, magnesium and vitamin E. It contains fibre and is low in gluten.

## Pulses (Legumes)

The main pulses available in this country are red, brown or green (continental) lentils, yellow or green split peas and a huge variety of beans.

Pulses can be eaten in a variety of dishes or sprouted to produce nutritious, vitamin-rich sprouts for use in salads (see p. 101).

Soya beans are used to produce many different products with an excellent nutritive value (see p. 96).

### Nutritional value

Pulses are an excellent source of protein, carbohydrate, B-vitamins, sodium, potassium, magnesium, calcium, iron, phosphorus, copper and zinc. They are low in fat, contain essential fibre, and like grains, are relatively cheap protein sources.

The protein availability of pulses is significantly increased when they are eaten with either nuts or grains. The soya bean is unique in that it is the only known vegetable food to contain the eight essential amino-acids in the correct proportions (see p. 21).

### Tips for cooking

1 Pulses soak up a lot of liquid during cooking and most beans require some form of pre-soaking prior to being cooked.

**2**   A pressure cooker is invaluable when cooking pulses as it reduces the cooking time by two-thirds. Beans may be cooked from the dry state without pre-soaking in a pressure cooker.

**3**   Salt or acids (e.g. vinegar, lemon juice, tomatoes) should not be added during the cooking of pulses as they tend to toughen the skins which consequently increases cooking time.

**4**   All pulses should be thoroughly washed before cooking to remove dust and grit — this can be done in a sieve or by swirling the pulses in a bowl of water. Some may require several rinses before the water runs clear.

**5**   Cooking water from pulses should never be discarded as it contains valuable vitamins and starch which makes it an ideal thickener for soups, casseroles and sauces. It will keep several days in the fridge.

**6**   Cooked pulses may be used immediately, stored in the fridge for 2–3 days or frozen and used as required after thawing.

### Digestibility

Pulses are known for being indigestible and causing flatulence, especially in people who are not used to a wholefood diet.

This is because most pulses (beans in particular) contain very complex carbohydrates which are difficult for the body to break down in the stomach and small intestines in the usual way. These carbohydrates have to be digested in the large intestine by bacteria present there. Unfortunately this process also results in the liberation of various gases (including methane), causing flatulence.

Careful cooking and rinsing will help reduce these problems — it has been found the smaller, quicker cooking varieties cause less flatulence.

### Storage

Pulses have a long shelf-life provided they are kept in cool, airtight containers and can therefore be bought in bulk more cheaply. After 12 months, pulses harden, start to shrivel and take longer to cook. It is advisable to buy from a shop with a high turnover and use within 6–8 months. Pressure cooking usually softens old beans and makes them more palatable.

All pulses vary in cooking times, flavour, texture and uses in the diet. The following information explains how to prepare and use the various kinds of pulses to help you get used to handling them.

Soya beans are dealt with separately (see p. 96) as they are used to produce so many products.

### Lentils

Lentils cook quickly so presoaking is not really necessary.

HOW TO COOK

Wash thoroughly (lentils usually require several rinses).
Cover with water or unsalted stock. Bring to the boil and skim off any froth.
Lower heat and simmer, covered, until the lentils are soft and swollen, 15–20 min for red lentils; 20–30 for brown/green lentils.
Add more liquid during cooking if lentils are going dry.

USES

Red lentils — go mushy when cooked therefore ideal for bakes, burgers, pâtés, shepherd's pie, stews etc.
Green/brown lentils — hold shape better when cooked so use for pies, casseroles, curries, sauces.

### Split peas

Take longer to cook than lentils so may be presoaked.

If presoaking, cover the split peas with boiling water and stand for 1 hour.
Wash or rinse thoroughly.
Cook as for lentils: 45–60 min unsoaked or 30 min if soaked.

USES

Go mushy on cooking so ideal for bakes, burgers, pâtés, stews and soups.

## Beans

Need to be soaked prior to cooking to reduce cooking time and aid digestibility.

SOAKING

*Method 1*
Wash thoroughly
Soak overnight (8–10 hours) in plenty of cold water. Discard soaking water.
Rinse thoroughly before cooking.
*Method 2*
Wash thoroughly.
Soak in boiling water for one hour. Discard water.
Rinse thoroughly before cooking.

HOW TO COOK

Cover with unsalted stock or water. Bring to the boil and skim off any froth (a drop of oil in water reduces froth).
Lower heat and simmer uncovered until beans are soft (see Table 9).
Drain and reserve cooking water for stock.

*Note* If you suffer from flatulence when you eat beans it will be beneficial to rinse the beans after the first and second boiling. Bring to the boil, drain, rinse thoroughly and repeat two or three times before simmering undisturbed.

Red kidney beans must be *boiled vigorously for ten minutes* before being simmered to destroy toxic substances they contain which are harmful if eaten.

PRESSURE COOKING BEANS

All beans can be pressure cooked in about one-third of the normal cooking time. If over pressure cooked, beans will turn into a soggy mush so it is advisable to check the beans after 5–10 minutes to see if they are done until you are experienced enough to judge exactly how long they will take.
*Method 1*
Presoak beans as already described.
Rinse and place in pressure cooker. Cover with unsalted

stock or water (a drop of oil will prevent froth from clogging up the air vent of the cooker).

Bring the beans to *high* pressure (15 lb) and cook for the required time (see Table 9).

*Method 2*

Wash dry beans thoroughly and do not soak.

Cover beans with unsalted water or stock and bring to *high* pressure (15 lb).

Pressure cook for 20–30 mins. depending on the size of bean.

USES OF BEANS

*Whole* — casseroles, stews, salads, pies, curries, sauces.
*Mashed/puréed* — burgers, roasts, shepherd's pie, pasties, etc.

**Table 9.**   Cooking times for beans.

| Bean | Normal cooking | Pressure cooking (soaked) |
|---|---|---|
| *Small beans* Mung, adzuki, black eye, field beans. | 30–45 min | 5–10 min |
| *Medium beans* Borlotti, kidney, canellini, flagolet, ful medames, lima. | 45–60 min | 10–15 min |
| *Large beans* Haricot, chick peas, butter, pinto, broad | $1\frac{1}{4}$–$1\frac{1}{2}$ hours | 15 min |
| *Soya beans* | 3–4 hour | 25–35 min |

## Soya beans and their products (Table 10)

Soya beans were first grown and used in China where they are considered to be one of the five sacred grains (rice, wheat, barley and millet are the others). They are still grown extensively in the Far East but the USA is now the world's largest producer of soya beans.

Soya beans are the only known vegetable food to contain the eight essential amino-acids in the correct proportions needed by the body. They produce more protein per acre than any other crop.

Unfortunately they are the hardest of all the beans to deal with and require prolonged soaking, 3–4 hours cooking and careful seasoning to make them palatable as they have a very strong flavour. They are also the least digestible bean and often cause flatulence.

However, they are extremely versatile and have been fully utilised to make a wide variety of products which are delicious, nutritious, easily digested and with no undesirable side effects.

**Table 10.** Soya products.

| What is it? | Uses in the diet | Storage |
| --- | --- | --- |
| *Soya grits* | | |
| Precooked soya beans which have been broken up in a similar way to bulgar wheat (Table 8) | Only take a few minutes to cook so can be added to stews and casseroles to improve nutritive value. | 12 months. |
| *Soya splits* | | |
| Soya beans split in half like split peas. May be raw or cooked. | Add to casseroles etc. | 12 months. |
| *Soya flour* | | |
| Rich yellow flour made from ground beans. Has fairly high fat content and is rich in protein. Must be cooked as contains harmful enzymes in raw state. Precooked soya flour available. | Used to enhance protein content of cakes, pastries, biscuits, batters. Can be made into vegan 'cheese' | Use within 6 months. |
| *Soya oil* | | |
| Polyunsaturated and cholesterol free. Rich in vitamins (especially E) and minerals especially if cold pressed and not refined. | Use for all cooking and salad dressings. Used in margarine manufacture. | Keeps 6–8 months unrefined or 12 months refined. |
| *Soya milk* | | |
| Made from cooked, puréed and then strained soya beans. Alternative to cows | Use as for cows milk on cereal, in sauces, puddings and to glaze pies. | Keeps 6–8 days refrigerated once opened. Tetrapak long life soya milks keep 6–12 months unopened. |

| What is it? | Uses in the diet | Storage |
| --- | --- | --- |

milk — has similar protein, iron, calcium and B-vitamins content but less fat and no cholesterol. More easily digested than cows milk and does not cause allergies. May be fortified with vitamin $B_{12}$. Available in liquid or dried powder form — numerous brands available.

*Miso*

| | | |
| --- | --- | --- |
| A bacteria-fermented soya product that originated in the Far East. Several types available depending on grain that is mixed with soya (Table 11). A natural source of vitamin $B_{12}$. Contains enzymes that aid digestion and is rich in protein. | Used to flavour soups, stews, pâtés, roasts, etc. *Must not be boiled* or beneficial enzymes will be destroyed. | Keeps indefinitely unrefrigerated. |

*Tempeh*

| | | |
| --- | --- | --- |
| A mould-fermented soya bean product which looks like a piece of white cake. Has very savoury flavour (mild or strong depending on length of fermentation) so not suitable for sweet dishes. High in protein, low fat, no cholesterol and contains natural vitamin $B_{12}$. Usually sold deep-frozen. Delicacy in the Far East where it is known as 'Bean Cake'. | Usually deep fried like tofu (see p. 100) but can be crumbled, pureed for burgers, roasts, etc. Can be cubed and served in salads. | Keeps up to 7 days refrigerated once opened and thawed. |

| What is it? | Uses in the diet | Storage |
| --- | --- | --- |

*Soy sauce*
Another bacteria-fermented soya product. Has rich savoury flavour and contains natural vitamin $B_{12}$ and beneficial enzymes that aid digestion. Genuine *tamari* soy sauce is the liquid collected at the bottom of the keg during miso production. It is gluten free and has a stronger flavour than *shoyu* soy sauce which contains wheat. Imitation soy sauce is made from hydrolysed vegetable protein coloured with caramel and is nutritionally inferior.

Soy sauce enhances the flavour of all vegan dishes. It can be used to make dips, season vegetables or as a base for stock. Add to bakes, burgers, casseroles, soups, etc.

Keeps indefinitely unrefrigerated.

*TVP (textured vegetable protein)*
Soya beans which have been cooked and processed to produce a meat-textured product. Available in mince or chunk form in variety of flavours. Sold dried and has to be reconstituted with water. Useful when first embarking on a vegan diet.

Use in pies, burgers, spaghetti sauces, casseroles, shepherd's pie, etc.

Keeps 12 months in dry state. Once reconstituted use within 3 days

*Soya dessert, yoghurt and icecream*
Recently introduced onto the market — made from soya milk or tofu. Soya dessert made by Provamel in carob and vanilla flavours, yoghurts and icecreams in various fruit flavours.

Use as toppings for vegan desserts or serve on their own as a delicious, nutritious sweet.

*Dessert*
Keeps 6–12 months unopened in tetrapak. Once opened use within 7 days. *Yoghurt* Keeps 7 days. *Icecream* See manufacturers label.

## Tofu

Tofu is soya bean curd. It originated in the Far East where it has been a staple food of the Chinese and Japanese for hundreds of years. Tofu is made from soya milk which has been curdled by a coagulant in a similar way that cheese is made from cows milk curdled by calves rennet.

### NUTRITIONAL VALUE

Tofu is an excellent source of protein which can be improved even more by combining with grains, e.g. rice, breadcrumbs, pastry. It also contains B-vitamins, vitamin E, calcium, phosphorus, magnesium, potassium, has a low fat content, no cholesterol and is 95% digestible.

At approximately 60–80 pence for 10 oz. (275 g) it is a cheap, healthy, nutritious and versatile alternative to dairy produce.

### VARIETIES AVAILABLE

Tofu can be bought from health stores or Chinese delicatessens. It may also be made at home fairly easily.

In the Far East there are over 20 different types available but in the West the two most commonly found varieties are *regular (firm) tofu*, made from normal soya milk and a coagulant to produce a solid slab of white curd which is usually sold fresh — some shops sell a smoked variety; and *silken (soft) tofu*, made from rich, thick soya milk and less coagulant to produce a soft, creamy curd; usually sold in long-life tetrapaks.

### STORAGE

*Fresh tofu*: always purchased covered in water which is essential to keep it fresh and prevent it going sour and slimy. Once the pack is opened the water must be changed daily. Fresh tofu keeps 7–10 days refrigerated.

*Silken tofu*: the unopened tetrapak will keep for at least 6 months unrefrigerated (see the sell-by date on the pack). Once opened treat as for fresh tofu.

*Freezing tofu*: tofu will freeze, but goes brown and slightly chewy in texture. On thawing as much water as possible

100

should be squeezed out of the tofu.

Frozen tofu can be used in sauces, curries and casseroles where the change in texture will be disguised. It should not be deep fried as the porous texture causes it to soak up a lot of oil making it very greasy.

USES OF TOFU

Tofu is very bland but absorbs the flavour of other sweet or savoury ingredients which makes it very tasty and versatile.

Strips of tofu can be marinaded in soy sauce with ginger, garlic, herbs or spices before using it in a variety of dishes.

It may be firmed up for deep frying by placing between two towels with a weighted plate on top for a few hours. It can then be sliced and used as required.

The basic uses of tofu are: *mashed* – burgers, bakes, stir-fried dishes; *creamed* — flans, desserts, mayonnaise, whips; *sliced/cubed* — curries, pasta sauces, raw in salads; *deep fried* — stir-fry dishes, sauces, casseroles.


## Beansprouts

Most beans, seeds and grains can be sprouted for use in salads or crunchy stir-fried dishes.

Sprouting beans improves their digestibility and increases their vitamin and mineral content considerably. It also breaks down phytic acid present in the outer skins of beans and grains that reduces iron and calcium absorption by the body.

Some beans produce more palatable sprouts than others, the most popular and well known being mung beansprouts which are found in most supermarkets.


NUTRITIONAL VALUE

Sprouted beans are rich in vitamin C, one vitamin that is lacking in the dry bean. They also contain vitamins A, B-group and E and the minerals calcium, iron, magnesium, chlorine, sodium, phosphorus and potassium. Beansprouts are rich in protein, easily digestible and less gas forming than dry beans.

The most nutritious sprouts are soya bean sprouts as they have the highest protein content. In order to maximise nutritional value sprouts should be eaten within 7 days of germination as the vitamin content falls again after this period.

101

Beansprouts are also alleged to have detoxifying properties and provide resistance to disease.

Sprouts can be grown easily at home which guarantees freshness as they can be harvested at the peak of condition.

Salad sprouters can be purchased in some health stores. These are ideal for families or people who eat a lot of sprouts as several types can be grown at once. A simpler and cheaper way is to use a jam jar.

**1** Put a tablespoonful of beans on a plate and pick over to remove stones. Wash thoroughly.

**2** Place beans in a wide-necked jam jar and fill with water. Soak overnight.

**3** Drain and rinse beans. Put beans back in jar and cover with a piece of sterilized muslin, cheesecloth or nylon net secured with a rubber band.

**4** Tilt the jar on its side to allow the beans to drain. Place in a warm, well ventilated place out of direct sunlight.

**5** Rinse the beans 2–3 times a day and keep the jar tilted. Rinsing keeps the beans moist and removes impurities given off by the growing process.

**6** After 2–3 days the beans should start to sprout. Check for mould and rotting.

**7** Continue rinsing daily until the sprouts are ready to harvest (a further 2–4 days depending on type). Rinse sprouts before eating and remove any ungerminated beans.

**8** Sprouts will keep in the fridge for up to 4 days in a plastic bag.

*Note* it is important to buy only organically grown beans which have not been treated with pesticides or fungicides which could be harmful if eaten and inhibit sprouting.

## Vegetables

Vegetables are a valuable source of vitamins A, B-group and C and minerals sodium, potassium, iron, copper, calcium, phosphorus and zinc.

Vegetables are low in protein and fat (with the exception of avocado pears) because they have a high water content. They do provide some carbohydrate (especially root vegetables) and essential fibre.

Besides being an ingredient in savoury cooked dishes, raw or lightly cooked vegetables should be eaten daily. Almost all vegetables can be eaten raw and the variety of salads that can be made is enormous — even in the winter. Fruits, nuts and cooked grains can be added for variety and to improve the nutritive value.

In order to obtain the maximum amount of vitamins and minerals as possible a wide variety of vegetables should be eaten. With today's modern methods of import and export the range of vegetables in the greengrocers shop is ever increasing although the more exotic ones are obviously more expensive and relatively few will be organically grown (see below).

### Tips for preparing and buying vegetables

**1** If vegetables are to be eaten cooked they should only be boiled, steamed or fried for the shortest time possible to conserve vitamins.

**2** Cooking water should never be discarded as water soluble vitamins B and C will be leached out during cooking. It can be used for stock or gravy.

**3** Vegetables generally contain more minerals than fruits and these are concentrated in the skin and outer layers. Consequently vegetables should not be peeled but just scrubbed or washed wherever possible.

**4** Damaged, bruised or wilted vegetables will have a depleted nutritive value and should be avoided even if they are in the 'bargain basket'.

**5** Vegetables that are tightly wrapped in cling film have a lower nutritive value than unwrapped ones.

### Storing vegetables

Salad and green vegetables keep best if stored unwrapped in the bottom of the refrigerator. Airy, cool vegetable racks out of direct sunlight are best for storing root vegetables, onions and garlic.

### Organic vegetables

Organic vegetables are grown on chemical free soil and are consequently free of the risks of pesticide, insecticide or fungicide residues. Organic vegetables are also beneficial to the environment as they do not upset the natural nitrogen balance of the soil.

Although they may not be perfectly and uniformly shaped like non organically grown vegetables found in supermarkets, they have superior flavour and contain a more balanced level of minerals. Vegetables grown on soils that have been treated with mineral fertilisers will absorb minerals from the soil in unbalanced quantities which may upset the natural mineral balance in the body of the consumer and eventually results in a weak soil with low fertility.

Some organic vegetables may be grown with animal manure from intensive farms or fertilisers containing dried blood or bone meal. They are therefore unacceptable to vegans. It is advisable to check with the supplier first and if possible buy vegetables only from local organic farmers where standards are guaranteed. Being labelled 'organic' is not a guarantee that vegetables have been 'veganically' produced.

## Fruit

### Fresh fruit

Fresh fruit and fruit juices are the most important source of vitamin C in the diet. They also supply appreciable quantities of vitamins A and B-group and minerals sodium, calcium, phosphorus, magnesium, iron, copper and zinc.

Fruit has an extremely high water content so it is low in protein and fat but it does contain carbohydrates (in the form of sugars) and essential fibre.

The taste and refreshing quality of fruits is due to the various acids they contain — e.g. citric acid in oranges, grapefruits and lemons. Contrary to popular belief however, fruit does not cause acidity in the body as the minerals in fruit have a neutralising effect.

Fresh fruit and juices should be consumed daily.

TIPS FOR BUYING AND PREPARING FRUIT

**1** The minerals in fruit are concentrated mainly in the skin. To obtain maximum nutritive value fruit should not be peeled but just washed and eaten raw.

**2** Cooked fruit loses most of its vitamin B and C, partly through exposure to the air and partly by dissolving into cooking liquid. Fruit should therefore be stewed on a low heat for the minimal amount of time and in as little liquid as possible. The liquid should not be discarded but eaten with the fruit.

**3** Bruised or damaged fruit and fruit which has been cut and exposed to the air (e.g. melons and pineapples which are often sold in halves) have a lower vitamin content.

### STORAGE

Soft fruit should be stored in the refrigerator and preferably eaten the same day as purchased. Fruit with thicker skins such as oranges, bananas, apples and pears can be stored at room temperature.

## Dried fruit

Dried fruits, e.g. apricots, figs, prunes, dates, sultanas and raisins are a valuable source of iron and B-vitamins. They are also a concentrated energy supply because of the sugar they contain.

Prunes and dried apricots are one of the best plant sources of carotene (pro-vitamin A). All dried fruits act as a natural laxative because they are high in dietary fibre.

### USES OF DRIED FRUIT

Dried fruit can be added raw to breakfast cereals or cooked and used in desserts, cakes and biscuits.

Most do not require overnight soaking and may be stewed in fruit juice or water for up to 30 minutes until plump and soft. They can then be used in desserts or eaten as they are for a delicious, nutritious sweet. Dried fruit purée (especially date) makes an excellent mineral-rich sweetener as an alternative to sugar.

### BUYING DRIED FRUITS

If possible buy only organically grown dried fruit as this is free from pesticide and fungiside residues. Avoid fruit (particularly apricots) that has been treated with sulphur containing chemicals to preserve the colour as sulphur destroys B-vitamins. Likewise, fruits washed in mineral oil to make them shiny and attractive (especially raisins, currants and sultanas) should be avoided because mineral oil interferes with the absorption of calcium and phosphorus in the body and binds itself to fat-soluble vitamins A, D, E and K causing them to be excreted unabsorbed.

STORAGE

Dried fruit will keep for 8–12 months in cool, airtight containers but is better if used before this time as some (especially figs) tend to go 'sugary' in appearance due to the presence of natural yeasts and moulds. Although this is not harmful and can be washed off, very old dried fruit may begin to ferment and taste decidedly strange!

# 5

# FLAVOURING VEGAN FOODS

## Flavouring Ingredients

Flavouring vegan dishes is very important not only to make food appetising and palatable but to stimulate the production of saliva in the mouth. Saliva contains enzymes which start the process of breaking food down before it reaches the stomach, an important part of the digestive process.

Some vegan foods such as tofu, beans and grains have a fairly bland flavour which is greatly enhanced by the addition of various flavourings, herbs and spices.

When first embarking on a vegan diet it is quite difficult to know which flavourings to use to make foods tasty. I hope the tips in Table 11 will be useful to new and experienced vegans alike.

**Table 11.** Flavouring ingredients.

| Ingredient | How to use it |
| --- | --- |
| *Yeast extract*<br>A very concentrated, savoury paste. Contains B-vitamins, protein, potassium. Some have added vitamin $B_{12}$. | Most commonly used flavouring in all vegan dishes. Can be added as a paste to burgers, bakes, roasts etc. or dissolved in hot water to make a stock for casseroles, soups, etc. |
| *Soya sauce*<br>Authentic soya sauce should be matured at least one and a half years and contain no additives. There are two types: *shoyu*, made from soya beans and wheat; *tamari*, the liquid | Adds savoury, salty flavour to all dishes. Easily mixed in as it is a liquid. |

that collects at the bottom of the keg during miso production.
Only made from soya beans so suitable for those allergic to wheat.

Soy sauce is a fermented food so it contains enzymes beneficial to digestion. Tamari is stronger than shoyu. All authentic soy causes provide B-vitamins including vitamin $B_{12}$. Commercial soy sauce is made from hydrolysed vegetable protein and caramel and has a lower nutritive value.

### Vegetable stock

Paste, cubes or powder made from concentrated dried vegetables and spices. Most contain salt but some salt-free varieties are available.

Dissolve in boiling water according to instructions on pack and use in casseroles, soups, for binding roasts and burgers or for cooking grains and pulses to add flavour.

### Miso

A fermented soya bean paste that originated in Japan. The soya beans are fermented for 6 months to 3 years with various grains such as rice, barley and wheat to give a rich, savoury brown paste of varying flavour. In Japan there are over thirty varieties but the most common ones available here are: *Mugi Miso*, soya and barley; dark brown, medium flavour. *Hatcho Miso*, soya beans alone; black/brown, strongest flavour. *Genmai Miso*, soya and rice; red brown, milder flavour.

Miso is rich in protein, contains natural vitamin $B_{12}$ and is a 'live' food due to bacteria and enzymes present during fermentation. It is therefore beneficial to digestion. It is fairly expensive but only a small amount is needed so it lasts a long time. Miso keeps indefinitely and does not need refrigerating.

Miso *must not be boiled* or the beneficial enzymes it contains will be destroyed. It can be added as a *paste* to bakes and roasts and stirred in or dissolved in *warm water* to add to casseroles etc. It should be added at *the end of cooking time* and the dish just warmed to serving temperature and not boiled.

### Tomato purée

Concentrated paste that adds rich tomato flavour to all savoury

Stir into bakes, roasts, soups, sauces etc.

| Ingredient | How to use it |
|---|---|

dishes. Thickens sauces and casseroles. Salt-free varieties available. Refrigerate on opening to prevent mould growth.

*Wholegrain Mustard, Chutney, Pickle*
Preserves made from vegetables, vinegars and spices. May be hot or mild. Give tangy spicy flavour to curries, sauces, casseroles etc. Choose additive-free brands.

Stir in a little at a time to give a lift to curries, casseroles, bakes, sauces etc.

*Fresh Garlic*
Related to the onion family. *Bulbs* of garlic contain several individual *cloves* encased in a pink or white papery skin. Garlic gives a delicious aromatic flavour to all savoury dishes and is very beneficial to the digestion. Cooked garlic has a more subtle flavour than raw as the pungent oils contained in the raw clove are driven off by heat.

Whole cloves may be cooked without cutting — this inhibits the release of oils and gives a sweet nutty flavour that does not leave an odour on the breath. In the Far East whole cloves are deep fried and eaten by the plateful!

Peel the papery skin off, then crush, chop or slice and add to any dish.

Whole cloves can be cooked in casseroles and removed before serving to give added flavour. Garlic is more aromatic if gently sautéed in oil or margarine before using. It must not be browned though or the flavour is spoilt.

*Fresh ginger*
A knobbly brown root grown in the Far East. Found in most good grocers and supermarkets. Has a pungent aroma and delicious spicy flavour. When peeled the flesh is bright yellow, juicy and has a stringy texture.

Peel, then chop or grate finely and add to curries, sauces, stir-fried dishes, casseroles etc. to give a suble spiced flavour. Can be sautéed before use like garlic.

*Lemon rind*
The yellow zest (not the white pith) from ripe lemons. Adds a tangy flavour to all dishes.

Grate finely and add to roasts, burgers, curries, sauces etc.

# Herbs and Spices

Herbs and spices have been used in cookery since the time of the ancient Egyptians. They owe their lovely aromatic flavour to the *essential oils* they contain. These organic oils are produced in tiny glands within the plant, and some are only released on heating.

Many herbs are native to Britain and have been used for years but the majority of our spices are imported from the Middle and Far East and are not so widely known. There is no real distinction between herbs and spices as spices are generally the seeds, roots, flowers or fruits of herbs. Herbs are usually thought of as leaves, but may also be seeds. They are used mainly in savoury dishes but spices may be either sweet or savoury.

Fresh herbs give a superb flavour to salads and all cooked dishes. Many can be grown easily at home in a window box or small garden. Some supermarkets and all good herbalists stock a range of fresh herbs. They need to be washed and chopped before using.

Some people prefer to use dried herbs as they are more convenient to use straight from the jar and easier to store. The power of dried herbs should never be under estimated – they are very concentrated so a small pinch will usually be sufficient. In recipes using fresh herbs, halve the quantity if you are using dried ones.

Most spices are sold dried, either as whole seeds or ground into powders. They have an attractive colour and pungent aroma. Spices are more powerful than herbs so use sparingly. An over-herbed dish may be acceptable but if over-spiced, food looses all its original flavour and is overpowered by the spices.

## Buying and storing

Prices vary from place to place but generally, the cheapest place to buy dried herbs and spices is the health store or Indian shops where they are sold by the ounce from large sacks or jars. Small jars with attractive packaging (as sold in many supermarkets) may look nice but are usually 3–4 times the price of those sold loose.

Buy from a shop with a high turnover for maximum freshness and store in a cool, dry, dark place to preserve the aroma and colour. Herbs and spices will keep for years but do go musty with age so are better used within 8–12 months.

## Which herbs and spices to use?

The herbs and spices in Table 12 are the ones I like to use in cooking. They are commonly found in health stores, herbalists, delicatessens and Indian stores.

More exotic, unusual herbs are not so widely available but if you grow them in your garden, feel free to substitute them for any I have listed.

**Table 12.** Herbs and spices.

| | Herbs |
| --- | --- |
| Basil (leaf) | Sweet herb. Good with tomato dishes, rice, pasta, sauces, peas, beans, broccoli, sweetcorn, aubergine, asparagus, courgettes. |
| Bay (leaf) | Bay leaves only release their subtle, mellow flavour when they are heated. Excellent for flavouring soups, stews, casseroles and tomato dishes whilst they are cooking but must be removed before serving as whole leaves can damage the stomach if swallowed. Ground bay can be added to any savoury dish. |
| Chervil (leaf) | Related to parsley. Has a subtle flavour that goes well with tarragon, chives and basil. Lovely in salads and dips or with broccoli, peas, spinach, asparagus. |
| Chives (leaf) | Related to onions, leeks and garlic so has a mild oniony flavour. Dried chives can be added to any savoury dish. Fresh chives are delicious in salads, sauces or as a garnish. They should be added at the end of cooking time for maximum flavour. |
| Dill (seeds and leaves) | Dill leaf (or 'weed') is lovely with potatoes, cabbage, celery, cauliflower, broccoli, cucumber, beetroot, sprouts, beans and turnip. Dill seeds are very aromatic and are good in sauces and salads or sprinkled over cooked vegetables to add flavour and texture. |
| Fennel (seeds and leaves) | Fennel leaf (or 'weed') has a characteristic aniseed flavour that is delicious in salads, casseroles and stuffings. Fennel seeds are more pungent and add flavour to rice dishes, salads, sauces, curries and casseroles. Can also be sprinkled onto bread before baking and used to make fennel tea which is very therapeutic. |

| | |
|---|---|
| Fines herbes (leaves) | A mixture of marjoram, sage, basil, thyme, fennel seed, parsley and chives used as a general purpose seasoning in all savouries. |
| Marjoram (leaf) | Sweet herb. Good with rice, pasta, tomato dishes, soups, sauces, carrots, spinach, peas, onions, courgettes, asparagus. |
| Mint (leaf) | Fresh mint is the traditional accompaniment to new potatoes, peas and carrots. Can also be made into mint sauce to serve with nut roast for a change. |
| Mixed herbs (leaves) | A general purpose mixture of sage, oregano, parsley, thyme, basil, chives and sometimes mint. Use in any savoury dish. |
| Oregano (leaf) | Oregano is wild Marjoram. It has a more pungent flavour than marjoram and goes well with tomatoes, beans, peas, onions, corn, cabbage, spinach. Use sparingly. |
| Parsley (leaf) | Fresh parsley adds piquancy to any savoury dish, soup or sauce. Also used as a garnish. Contains useful amounts of iron, calcium, vitamin C and carotene (provitamin A). Parsley blends well with other herbs. Dried parsley does not have such a good flavour as fresh. |
| Rosemary (leaf) | Has characteristic fragrant aroma and flavour. Lovely with roast or sautéed potatoes, spinach, peas, in bakes and stuffings. |
| Sage (leaf) | Delicious flavour but can be overpowering so use sparingly. Excellent in roasts, burgers and stuffings and with beans, onions, peas, potatoes, pumpkin, marrow and tomatoes. |
| Savory (leaf) | Savory is similar to thyme but has a more delicate flavour. It's other name is 'beanherb' because it goes so well with beans, peas and lentils. Also nice with tomatoes, potatoes and in green salad. |
| Tarragon (leaf) | Has a very special taste so usually used alone and not mixed with other herbs. Very pungent so use sparingly. Delicious with mushrooms, leeks, in sauces and casseroles. Used to flavour tarragon vinegar which makes delicious salad dressings. Fresh tarragon is lovely in tomato salad. |
| Thyme (leaf) | Several types. Can be used in most dishes and has a delicate flavour. Good in lentil and pulse dishes, stuffings and with cabbage, carrots, green vegetables, tomatoes, onions, aubergines. |

---

### Spice

---

| | |
|---|---|
| Cardamom (fruit) | Very delicately flavoured seed used almost exclusively in sweet dishes, preserves and fruit jellies. Lovely in curries and roasts but very expensive so use sparingly. Green or black cardamom seeds are available. Sold ground or whole. |

112

| | |
|---|---|
| Carraway (seed) | A very pungent seed that releases more aroma if it is dry roasted before use. Used in casseroles, goulash, cakes, biscuits and with potatoes or green vegetables (especially cabbage). Used to flavour pickles. |
| Cayenne pepper (fruit) | A very hot, red pepper similar to chilli. Used in curries, hot dishes, sauces, pickles, salad dressing. Use sparingly. |
| Chilli powder (fruit) | Ground dried chillis. Very hot so use sparingly. Used in curries, goulash, hot dishes, pickles, sauces. |
| Cinnamon (bark) | A sweet smoky spice used mainly in desserts, especially jams, jellies and with apples. Whole cinnamon sticks (quills) can be infused in fruit juices or soya milk to add flavour to sweet sauces and custards. |
| Cloves (flower) | Pungent spice that adds a characteristic flavour to both sweet and savoury dishes. Good in steamed puddings, jams, apple pie, curries and spicy rice dishes. Also nice with carrots, beetroot, marrow, pumpkin, sweet potatoes. Whole cloves can be tied in a muslin bag for easy removal from sauces etc. Ground cloves available. |
| Coriander (seeds and leaves) | A pungent, sweet seed. Ground coriander is used in curries, roasts and many savouries. Can also be used in sweet dishes and soya milk puddings like nutmeg. Whole seeds can be crushed and added to sauces, casseroles or spiced drinks. Coriander leaf is a herb like parsley which features heavily in Mexican and Italian cooking. Delicious in soups and casseroles. |
| Cumin (seeds) | A smoky, pungent seed similar to carraway. Ground and used in curries and spiced dishes. Gives a characteristic flavour to pulse dishes, dips and pâtés. Whole seeds are crushed and used in casseroles and stews. They release more aroma on heating. |
| Curry powder | A commercially prepared mixture of spices including turmeric, coriander, cumin, chilli and cardamom. Available in various strengths. Buy only a good quality curry powder — cheap ones have a very poor flavour. Use in curries and to 'pep' up vegetable mixtures, burgers, pasty fillings etc. |
| Garam Masala | A mixture of spices including cumin, coriander, cloves, pepper and cardamom. Used in curries and spiced dishes and added near the end of cooking time to maximise flavour. |
| Ginger (root) | The ground dried root. Adds characteristic flavour to curries, stewed fruit, preserves, sweet dishes and cakes. The fresh root has a superior flavour (see p. 109). |

| | |
|---|---|
| Mace<br>(seed-coat) | Mace is the outer seed coat of nutmegs. It has a bright orange/yellow colour and is either sold as a powder or as whole 'blades'. It has a mild nutmeg flavour and is used mainly in savoury dishes. Goes well with beans, carrots, celery, swede, onions, cauliflower, potatoes and apples. Blades have to be heated to extract the flavour and are usually infused in liquids like cinnamon sticks to make sweet sauces. |
| Mixed spice | An aromatic mixture of sweet spices like nutmeg, cinnamon and cloves. Sometimes called 'Allspice'. Used in sweet dishes, custards, cakes and biscuits. |
| Mustard<br>(seed) | Used mainly as a condiment but can also be added to spicy dishes, cabbage, cucumber, beetroot, tomatoes, beans, onions, cauliflower, aubergine. Used in pickles and salad dressings. White mustard has a milder flavour than black mustard. Wholegrain mustards are an excellent addition to sauces, stuffings and casseroles, giving a spicy but not hot flavour. |
| Nutmeg<br>(fruit) | A strongly flavoured aromatic spice. Can be used in sweet and savoury dishes. Lovely in nutroast, burgers, pulse dishes, soya milk puddings and with asparagus, swede, sprouts, cabbage, marrow, spinach, corn, kale, pumpkin and mashed potato. Goes well with apples, pears, oranges and lemons. Freshly grated nutmeg has a superior flavour to the dry powder. |
| Paprika<br>(fruit) | A mild red pepper used in goulash, stews, potato and tomato dishes. Gives an 'earthy' flavour to salads, dips and soups. Makes a colourful garnish for any savoury dish. |
| Pepper<br>(fruit) | The most frequently used spice. White pepper is milder than black pepper and is made from the inner parts of the berry with the black husk removed. Pepper has a greater flavour when cooked. Freshly ground black pepper adds a unique flavour to all savoury dishes. |
| Turmeric<br>(root) | A pungent yellow spice with a smoky flavour. Related to ginger. Used mainly in curries and for colouring rice dishes but is also nice in dips, sauces, salad dressings, pickles and mustards. Use sparingly. |
| Vanilla<br>(fruit pods) | Vanilla essence is used exclusively in sweet dishes and custards to add flavour and aroma. It improves with age and must be added near the end of cooking time because it evaporates quickly on heating. Vanilla pods can be infused in liquids like cinnamon sticks to make sauces. Vanilla essences bought in supermarkets are synthetic and do not contain any vanilla at all. Genuine vanilla essences are very expensive so use sparingly. |

# 6

# RECIPES

As there are already numerous vegan and vegetarian cookery books available which contain vegan recipes for soups, starters, cakes, biscuits and salads, I have omitted these sections and concentrated solely on main courses and sweets which form the basis of all meals. I have chosen the dishes that have proved most popular with friends, guests, and students attending my classes — many of whom are not vegetarian or vegan — in the hope that they will appeal to everyone, everywhere, regardless of dietary habits and beliefs.

Wherever possible the main dishes already contain complementary proteins (see p. 22) but in the few instances where this is not the case I have given examples of how complementarity can be achieved.

I have recommended specific sauces to accompany dishes at the end of the recipe but feel free to experiment with any of the sauce recipes – they are all delicious!

Many vegan recipes, especially bakes and roasts, seem to be even more tasty when eaten the day after they have been made, due to the mingling of more subtle flavourings that occurs when the dish is left to stand for several hours. From a nutritional standpoint I would recommend you eat everything fresh but it does no harm occasionally for entertaining purposes to make dishes the day before. Also, in most cases the dishes are very versatile and leftovers from one meal can be made into something completely different for the next day. For example cold nut roast makes excellent burgers if shaped and fried; cold lentil roast can be used as a pie filling or sandwich spread; pasta sauce can be curried and served with rice the following day. There is plenty of scope for experimentation.

Virtually all the recipes can be frozen but I have indicated where this is not suitable. As spices and garlic intensify in flavour after prolonged freezing it is advisable to use frozen dishes within 2 months. Alternatively, if dishes are being made specifically for the freezer, cut down on the amount of spices you use and the dish will keep longer.

People who are sensitive to certain foods such as mushrooms or wheat may easily substitute other ingredients. Peppers or celery are good alternatives to mushrooms, and cooked rice, millet or gluten-free breadcrumbs can be substituted for wheat breadcrumbs in roasts, burgers and bakes. Slimmers may cut down on the fat content of many dishes by omitting the preliminary frying of onions, garlic, etc. in recipes where the ingredients are going to be baked afterwards such as roasts.

Finally, there are several basic ingredients that I use throughout the recipes because of their unequalled nutritional value, flavour and cooking qualities. These are listed in Table 13 as a guide but you may substitute your own favourite brands where applicable.

### Servings

All the recipes serve four people unless otherwise stated. However, depending on appetite, type of meal and number of courses, dishes may be stretched to six servings in most cases.

**Table 13.** Basic ingredients used in the recipes, and alternatives where applicable.

| Basic Ingredients | Alternative |
| --- | --- |
| Flour: 100% organically grown, stoneground is exclusively used. | 81% or wheatmeal flour |
| Margarine: *Granose* vegan margarine | Any other vegan brand |
| Soya milk: *Plamil* — concentrated, no-sugar variety | Any soya milk brand |
| Sugar: wherever possible I have avoided the use of sugar in dessert recipes. Where small amounts *are* necessary, I use good quality raw muscavado or molasses sugar | Soft brown sugar, malt extract, molasses, maple syrup, dried fruit puree, honey (if eaten). |
| Oil: 100% cold pressed sunflower oil is used for most recipes although I use virgin cold pressed olive oil in some dishes because of its superior flavour | Any pure vegetable oil or solid vegetable fat. |
| Stock: *Frigg's* stock cubes, *Vecon* concentrate | Any vegan stock cubes |
| Yeast extract: *Barmene* | Any with added Vitamin $B_{12}$ |

Miso: Mugi miso (soya and barley)     Any miso although
                                      some have a stronger flavour.

Soy sauce; any good quality, authentic shoyu (soya and wheat) or tamari (no wheat).

Salt: I never use salt in cooking, not only because it tends to overpower and impair the delicate flavour of many vegan dishes, but it also upsets the body's natural mineral balance and is associated with heart disease and high blood pressure. As your tastebuds become accustomed to vegan food you will find that yeast extract, miso and soy sauce will meet your seasoning requirements. When starting on a vegan diet try to use small amounts of biosalt, gomasio (sesame salt) or seasalt instead of table salt.

Herbs and spices: The ones quoted in the recipes are my personal favourites, but feel free to experiment with your own mixtures.

### Nutroast

A delicious, simple and very popular dish that is ideal for converting non-vegetarian friends.

    6 oz (175 g) wholemeal breadcrumbs
    6 oz (175 g) finely chopped nuts (e.g. hazels, walnuts, cashews)
    1 large onion, chopped
    1 clove garlic, crushed
    Knob margarine
    ¼ pint (150 ml) strong stock
    1 tablespoon tomato purée
    1 teaspoon yeast extract or miso
    Rind and juice 1 small lemon
    1 teaspoon each of sage, thyme and nutmeg
    Black pepper

117

## Method

Set oven to Gas 5/190°C/375°F.
Grease a 2 pint (1 litre) ovenproof dish or 2 lb (1 kilo) loaf tin.

- Fry onion and garlic in the margarine until soft.
- Add the nuts, breadcrumbs, tomato purée, yeast extract/miso, lemon rind and juice, herbs and nutmeg. Season well and mix thoroughly.
- Add enough stock to moisten and mix well (Add more stock for a moister roast and less for a firmer texture which can be sliced).
- Press into prepared dish and cover with foil. Bake 1 hour removing the foil for the last 15 minutes to brown the top.
- Serve with tomato or miso sauce (pages 239–40), potatoes and a salad or green vegetable.
- Can be frozen cooked or uncooked; thaw before baking.

*Variations*: grated cooking apple or carrots can be added for a change in flavour.

### Celebration Nut Roast with Lemon and Garlic Stuffing

This roast is very rich and will probably serve six depending on appetite and what vegetables are to accompany it. Especially good at Christmas with the traditional vegetables. Can also be eaten cold for buffets and picnics. (Serves 4–6.)

4 oz (100 g) wholemeal breadcrumbs
8 oz (225 g) finely ground nuts (e.g. hazels, brazils, almonds)
1 large onion, chopped
Knob margarine
1 heaped tablespoon flour
¼ pint (150 ml) soya milk
¼ pint (150 ml) stock
1 teaspoon yeast extract or miso
1 teaspoon nutmeg
Black pepper
*Stuffing:*
3 oz (75 g) wholemeal breadcrumbs
2 oz (50 g) melted margarine
½ small onion, grated
1 clove garlic, crushed
2 tablespoons fresh chopped parsley
Rind 1 lemon, finely grated

*Method*

Set oven to Gas 5/190°C/375°F.
Grease and line a 2 lb (1 kilo) loaf tin with a strip of grease-proof paper long enough to overhang at either end. Grease the paper well.

• *Make nutmeat first:* Fry the onion in the margarine until soft. Add the flour, stir and cook for 1 minute.
• Remove from heat and gradually add the milk and stock, stirring continuously to avoid lumps. Return to the heat and bring to the boil, stirring continuously until the sauce has thickened.
• Add the yeast extract/miso, nutmeg and pepper. Stir well.
• Add the nuts and breadcrumbs to the onion sauce and mix thoroughly to form a stiff but moist nutmeat.
• *Make stuffing:* Combine all the stuffing ingredients and mix well.
• Put half the nutmeat into the prepared tin and press down firmly. Pile the stuffing on top and press again. Finally put the remaining nutmeat on the stuffing and smooth the top.
• Bake for 1 hour until brown and firm. Cool slightly in tin.
• Run a knife round the roast then invert onto a serving plate. Remove the greaseproof paper and garnish with parsley and lemon wedges. Serve with sherry or mushroom and sherry sauce and the traditional vegetables.
• Can be frozen cooked or uncooked; thaw before baking.


**Yellow Pea and Hazelnut Roast**

A light, tasty roast suitable for a family meal, hot or cold.

8 oz (225 g) yellow split-peas, washed thoroughly
1 stock cube
2 bay leaves
2 teaspoons thyme
4 oz (100 g) ground hazelnuts
4 oz (100 g) wholemeal breadcrumbs
1 onion, finely chopped
2 cloves garlic, crushed
4 oz (100 g) mushrooms, sliced
1 tablespoon oil

2 teaspoons miso
1 tablespoon tomato purée
1 teaspoon ground mace
1 teaspoon coriander
Pepper

## *Method*

Set oven to Gas 5/190°C/375°F.
Grease a 2 pint (1 litre) ovenproof dish.

• Put the split peas, stock cube, bay leaves and thyme in a pan and cover with water. Bring to the boil, cover and simmer for 40 minutes until the peas are soft and mushy (add more water as necessary and stir regularly to prevent sticking).
• Fry the onion, garlic and mushrooms in the oil until soft then add to the split pea puree with the hazelnuts, breadcrumbs, miso, tomato purée, mace, coriander and pepper. Mix thoroughly.
• Pile into the prepared dish and smooth over.
• Cover with foil and bake for 45 minutes removing the foil for the last 10 minutes to brown the top.
• Serve with parsley and tarragon or tahini and miso sauce, boiled potatoes and green vegetables.
• Freeze uncooked; thaw before baking.

## Lentil, Walnut and Parsnip Roast

An interesting and tasty combination of flavours makes this nutritious roast ideal as a dinner party dish. Swede or carrot can be substituted for the parsnip if preferred.

8 oz (225 g) red lentils, thoroughly washed
1 stock cube
4 oz (100 g) walnuts, chopped
6 oz (175 g) parsnip, scrubbed and grated
4 oz (100 g) wholemeal breadcrumbs
1 onion, finely chopped
2 cloves garlic, crushed
1 tablespoon oil
3 tablespoons fresh chopped parsley
1 teaspoon nutmeg

1 teaspoon thyme
1 teaspoon yeast extract
1 tablespoon tomato purée
Black pepper

*Method*

Set the oven to Gas 5/190°C/375°F.
Grease a 2 pint (1 litre) ovenproof dish.

• Put the lentils in a pan with the stock cube and cover with water. Bring to the boil, skim off any froth, then cover and simmer on a low heat for 20 minutes until the lentils are soft and mushy. (Add more water as necessary and stir occasionally to prevent sticking.)
• Fry the onion and garlic in the oil until softening. Add to the lentil puree with the walnuts, parsnip, thyme, nutmeg, yeast extract, tomato puree, pepper and 2 oz (50 g) of the breadcrumbs.
• Pile into the prepared dish, smooth over and sprinkle the remaining breadcrumbs on top.
• Bake for 30 minutes until golden and crispy on top.
• Serve with boiled new potatoes or jacket potato and salad.
• Freeze raw, thaw and bake as above.

**Buckwheat and Brazil Nut Roast**

A very savoury roast with the characteristic flavour of buckwheat. Can be served hot or cold.

4 oz (100 g) buckwheat, roasted (see page 85) or bought ready roasted
1 stock cube
1 teaspoon sage
4 oz (100 g) ground brazil nuts
1 onion, finely chopped
2 carrots, grated
2 cloves garlic, crushed
4 oz (100 g) mushrooms, sliced
½ red pepper, chopped
1 tablespoon oil
2 tablespoons fresh chopped parsley

2 teaspoons nutmeg
1 tablespoon soy sauce
4 tablespoons stock
Pepper

## *Method*

Set oven to Gas 5/190°C/375°F.
Grease a 2 pint (1 litre) ovenproof dish.

• Put the buckwheat in a pan with the stock cube and sage.
Cover with water and bring to the boil. Cover and simmer on
a low heat for 20 minutes until the buckwheat is soft and
swollen. Stir regularly to prevent sticking and add more water
as necessary during cooking.
• Fry the onion, carrots, garlic, mushrooms and pepper in
the oil until soft.
• Mix the cooked buckwheat with the fried vegetables,
brazil nuts, parsley, nutmeg, soy sauce and pepper.
• Stir well and moisten with enough stock to make a soft, but
not wet, mixture (4 tablespoons should be enough).
• Pile into the prepared dish and smooth over.
• Cover with foil and bake for 30 minutes removing the foil
for the last 10 minutes to crisp the top.
• Serve with tomato, sweet and sour or barbecue sauce and
steamed green vegetables.
• Freeze raw, thaw and then bake.

## Spicy Bean and Nut Roast

This lightly spiced roast is extremely nutritious and very
filling but not quite so high in fat as a usual nutroast. Any
beans or nuts can be used and it is a good way of using up small
quantities of nuts and beans which would not be enough for
other recipes.

4 oz (100 g) beans (any type)
4 oz (100 g) chopped nuts (any type)
4 oz (100 g) wholemeal breadcrumbs
2 onions, finely chopped
2 cloves garlic, crushed
1 tablespoon oil
1 teaspoon yeast extract/miso

2 teaspoons pickle
1 teaspoon wholegrain mustard
1 tablespoon tomato purée
1 teaspoon coriander
1 teaspoon cumin
1 teaspoon garam masala
½ teaspoonful ground mace
Black pepper

## *Method*

Set the oven to Gas 5/190°C/375°F.
Grease a 2 pint (1 litre) ovenproof dish.

• Presoak and cook the beans according to previous instructions. Drain and reserve the liquid.
• Fry the onions and garlic in the oil until soft. Add the nuts, breadcrumbs, yeast extract/miso, pickle, mustard, tomato purée, coriander, cumin, garam masala, mace and pepper. Mix well.
• Liquidize or mash the beans to a smooth purée with about one tablespoon of the reserved liquid. Add to the nut mixture.
• Add about ¼ pint (150 ml) of the remaining bean water to make a fairly moist mixture and stir well.
• Pile into the prepared dish and smooth over. Bake uncovered for 45 minutes until well browned and firm.
• Serve with tomato or onion sauce, potatoes and salad.
• Can be frozen cooked or uncooked but use within 6 weeks because the spices will intensify in flavour after this time.
*Note*: This roast is even more delicious if made the day before it is required as the spices have time to 'mature'. If making this dish for a dinner party or something special, I would recommend making it in advance.


## Lentil and Mushroom Bake

A delicious, moist bake especially invented to convert anyone who says they don't like lentils! *This recipe is dedicated to Valerie.*

8 oz (225 g) red lentils, washed thoroughly
1 large onion, chopped

123

2 cloves garlic, crushed
4 oz (100 g) mushrooms, sliced
Knob margarine
1 teaspoon thyme
1 teaspoon coriander
1 tablespoon tomato purée
1 teaspoon yeast extract/miso
1 vegetable stock cube
4 oz (100 g) wholemeal breadcrumbs
Black pepper

### Method

Set oven to Gas 5/190°C/375°F.
Grease a 2 pint (1 litre) ovenproof dish.

- Put the lentils and stock cube in a pan, cover with water and cook until soft and mushy according to the instructions on page 121. (More water may need to be added but the mixture should not be too sloppy).
- Melt margarine and fry onion, garlic and mushrooms until soft.
- Add lentils, thyme, coriander, tomato puree, yeast extract/miso and pepper. Mix thoroughly.
- Add 2 oz (50 g) of the breadcrumbs and stir in.
- Pile the mixture into the prepared dish and smooth over the top. Sprinkle the remaining breadcrumbs on top.
- Bake for 30 minutes until top is brown and crispy.
- Serve with jacket or new potatoes and salad.
- Can be frozen uncooked or ready cooked.
- Any leftovers make a delicious sandwich spread.

### Bean Roast

A firm favourite! This very nutritious dish can be eaten hot or cold.

2–4 oz (150–100 g) wholemeal breadcrumbs
8 oz (225 g) white beans (eg. butter, haricot, black-eye)
Knob margarine
1 large onion, chopped
2 cloves garlic, crushed
4 oz (100 g) mushrooms, sliced
2 carrots, grated

1 cooking apple, peeled, cored and grated
Rind and juice 1 lemon
1 tablespoon tomato purée
1 teaspoon yeast extract or miso
1 teaspoon sage
1 teaspoon thyme
1 teaspoon nutmeg
1 tablespoon fresh chopped parsley
Pepper

## *Method*

Set oven to Gas 5/190°C/375°F.
Grease a 2 pint (1 litre) ovenproof dish.

• Presoak and cook the beans. Drain and reserve liquid.
• Melt margarine and fry onion, garlic, mushrooms, carrot and apple until softening.
• Add lemon rind and juice, tomato purée, yeast extract/miso, thyme, sage, parsley, nutmeg and pepper. Stir well.
• Liquidize or mash the beans adding a drop of cooking water if too dry (the mixture is better a bit on the wet side as it dries out a lot during baking).
• Mix the bean purée with the other ingredients and stir thoroughly.
• Add enough breadcrumbs to make a firm, but not too stiff, mixture. Pile into the prepared dish and smooth over.
• Cover with foil and bake for 1 hour, uncovering for the last 10 minutes to brown the top.
• Serve with tomato or mustard sauce made from the remaining bean water, jacket potatoes and green vegetables.
• Can be frozen uncooked or ready cooked.

## Nut and Mushroom Ring

A very attractive dinner party roast which can be served hot or cold. For a family meal it can be made in an ovenproof dish or loaf tin instead of a ring mould.

6 oz (175 g) wholemeal breadcrumbs
6 oz (175 g) ground nuts (e.g. hazels, cashews, walnuts)
1 large onion, finely chopped
1 clove garlic, crushed
4 oz (100 g) mushrooms, chopped
Knob margarine

1 tablespoon wholemeal flour
½ pint (275 ml) soya milk
3 tablespoons fresh chopped parsley
1 teaspoon sage
Rind 1 lemon
1 teaspoon yeast extract or miso
1 teaspoon mace or nutmeg
Black pepper

## Method

Set oven to Gas 5/190°C/375°F.
Grease well an 8″ (20 cm) ring mould or 2 pint (1 litre) ovenproof dish.

- Fry the onion, garlic and mushrooms in the margarine until soft.
- Add the flour, stir in and cook on a low heat for 1 minute.
- Remove from heat and add the milk, a little at a time, stirring vigorously to avoid lumps. (This sauce should be very thick or the ring will not hold its shape so do not add the milk too quickly — not all of it may be required).
- Return the pan to the heat and bring the sauce to the boil, stirring until it has thickened. Add the yeast extract/miso, sage, mace and pepper. Stir well.
- Stir in the breadcrumbs, nuts, lemon rind and parsley. Mix thoroughly.
- Press firmly into the prepared mould and smooth over.
- Bake for 1 hour until brown and firm.
- Cool for 5 minutes in the tin. Run a knife round the mould to loosen. Invert onto a plate and garnish with lemon slices and parsley.
- Serve hot with parsley sauce and vegetables or cold with pickles, relishes and salads.
- Can be frozen uncooked and baked on thawing or frozen ready cooked.

## Courgette, Mushroom and Smoked Tofu Bake

A delicious combination of flavours and textures. This recipe is very quick and easy to make and extremely nutritious.

1½ lb (625 g) courgettes, washed and sliced

8 oz (225 g) mushrooms, sliced
2 onions, sliced
2 cloves garlic, crushed
2 oz (50 g) margarine
12 oz (350 g) smoked tofu, drained
6 tablespoons cold water
6 oz (175 g) wholemeal breadcrumbs
Pepper
1 teaspoon ground mace
2 teaspoons coriander
1 tablespoon soy sauce

### Method
Set oven to Gas 5/190°C/375°F.
Grease a 2 pint (1 litre) ovenproof dish.

• Fry the courgettes, onions, mushrooms and garlic in the margarine for 5–10 minutes until softening and beginning to brown. Put to one side.
• Mash or liquidize the tofu to a smooth paste with the water, soy sauce, pepper, mace and coriander.
• Add the tofu purée to the vegetables in the pan and stir well to coat them thoroughly.
• Stir in 4 oz (100 g) of the breadcrumbs and turn into the prepared dish. Sprinkle the remaining breadcrumbs on top.
• Bake for 30 minutes until golden and crispy. Serve with salad and boiled new potatoes.
• Not suitable for freezing.

### Millet and Brazil Nut Bake

This tasty, nutritious roast is gluten-free and therefore suitable for those allergic to wheat.

8 oz (225 g) millet seed
1 stock cube
2 bay leaves
1 teaspoon sage
1 onion, chopped finely
2 cloves garlic, crushed
½ red pepper, sliced
4 oz (100 g) mushrooms, sliced
1 cooking apple, peeled, cored and grated
Knob margarine
4 oz (100 g) brazil nuts, ground or finely chopped

2 tablespoons fresh chopped parsley
1 tablespoon tomato purée
2 teaspoons coriander
1 tablespoon soy sauce
Pepper

## *Method*

Set the oven to Gas 5/190°C/375°F.
Grease a 2 pint (1 litre) ovenproof dish.

- Put the millet, stock cube, bay leaves and sage in a pan, cover with water and cook according to the previous instructions until soft and mushy. (Add more water as necessary and stir regularly to prevent sticking.)
- Meanwhile fry the onion, garlic, pepper, mushrooms and apple in the margarine until softening.
- Put the cooked millet in a bowl and add the fried vegetables, brazil nuts, parsley, tomato purée, coriander, soy sauce and pepper. Mix thoroughly and pile into the prepared dish. Smooth over.
- Cover with foil and bake for 45 minutes removing the foil for the last 10 minutes to brown the top.
- Serve with parsley and tarragon; mustard or tahini and miso sauce, potatoes and salad.
- Freeze raw, thaw and bake.

## Nut and Tofu Pudding

A delicious, filling and extremely nutritious dish. This pudding is lower in calories than a standard nutroast.

8 oz (225 g) wholemeal breadcrumbs
8 oz (225 g) *firm* tofu, mashed
4 oz (100 g) ground nuts (e.g. hazels, walnuts, brazils)
1 onion, finely chopped
2 cloves garlic, crushed
Knob margarine
¼ pint (150 ml) stock
Rind 1 small lemon
1 tablespoon soy sauce
1 teaspoon sage
1 teaspoon thyme
1 teaspoon coriander
Pepper to taste

## *Method*

Set oven to Gas 5/190°C/375°F.
Grease a 2 pint (1 litre) ovenproof dish.

- Melt the margarine and fry the onion and garlic until softening.
- Add the other ingredients and mix thoroughly adding more stock if the mixture seems too dry. (It should be quite stiff). Season well with pepper.
- Pile into the prepared dish, press down and cover with foil.
- Bake for 45 minutes removing the foil for the last 10 minutes to brown the surface.
- Serve with a spicy sauce such as barbecue, sweet and sour, curry or mustard and green vegetables.
- Can be frozen cooked or uncooked.


## Crispy Ratatouille Bake

Lovely rich ratatouille, layered with a crisp mixture of nuts and seeds, makes a very interesting dish.

2 tablespoons olive oil
1 aubergine, chopped into chunky pieces
1 red pepper, sliced
1 onion, chopped
2 cloves garlic, crushed
4 oz (100 g) mushrooms, sliced
4 courgettes, sliced
1 medium tin tomatoes, chopped
2 tablespoons tomato purée
1 teaspoon basil
12 oz (350 g) breadcrumbs
3 oz (75 g) brazil nuts, ground
3 oz (75 g) sunflower seeds
6 oz (175 g) margarine
2 tablespoons fresh chopped parsley
Pepper


## *Method*

Set oven to Gas 5/190°C/375°F.
Grease a 4 pint (2 litre) ovenproof dish.

- Fry the aubergine, pepper, onion, garlic, mushrooms and courgettes in the oil until softening. Cover and 'sweat' for 5 minutes.
- Add the tinned tomatoes, tomato purée, basil and pepper. Bring to the boil, cover and simmer on a low heat for 10 minutes until the vegetables are soft and the liquid thick.
- Melt the margarine on a low heat and stir in the breadcrumbs, nuts, seeds and parsley.
- Put one third of the breadcrumb mixture on the base of the prepared dish and pour half the ratatouille over.
- Add another layer of crumbs, then the rest of the ratatouille and finally a layer of crumbs. Bake for 20 minutes until the topping is brown and crispy.
- Serve with tahini and miso or lemon and coriander seed sauce, potatoes and a salad.
- Freeze unbaked, thaw and bake as above.


## Smoked Tofu Moussaka

This is a delicious vegan version of a traditional Greek dish. It is fairly rich so serve with a crisp salad and a light sweet.

> 2 aubergines
> Olive oil to fry
> 2 onions, chopped
> 2 cloves garlic, crushed
> 4 courgettes, chopped
> 1 red pepper, sliced
> 4 oz (100 g) mushrooms, sliced
> Medium tin tomatoes, chopped
> 2 tablespoons tomato purée
> 2 teaspoons oregano
> Pepper
> 8 oz (225 g) smoked tofu, drained
> 8 tablespoons water
> 2 teaspoons soy sauce
> 1 tablespoon tahini
> 2 tablespoons sesame seeds

### *Method*

Set oven to Gas 5/190°C/375°F.
Lightly grease a 2 pint (1 litre) ovenproof dish.

- Top and tail the aubergines and slice thickly into rounds. Heat 4–5 tablespoons of olive oil in a pan and fry the aubergine slices on both sides until brown. Add more oil as necessary (they will soak up quite a lot of oil). Drain on absorbent kitchen paper.
- Fry the onions, garlic, courgettes, pepper and mushrooms in any remaining oil (adding more if necessary) for a few minutes until softening.
- Add the tinned tomatoes, tomato purée, oregano and pepper. Bring to the boil, cover and simmer on a low heat for 10 minutes until the vegetables are cooked and the liquid has thickened. Put to one side.
- Put the tofu, water, soy sauce and tahini in a liquidizer and blend until smooth and creamy.
- Put a layer of aubergine slices on the base of the prepared dish and spread half the tomato sauce over.
- Add another layer of aubergines, then the rest of the sauce and finally a layer of aubergines. Pour the tofu mixture over the top.
- Sprinkle with sesame seeds and bake for 30 minutes until the tofu is set and golden brown. Serve immediately with a salad or lightly steamed green vegetables.
- Not suitable for freezing.

## Stuffed Vegetables

There are a variety of seasonal vegetables which lend themselves particularly well to being stuffed with a savoury filling that enhances their flavour and nutritive value. These are listed in Table 14 and suggested tasty fillings follow on pp. 132–137. Choose any of the sauces to complement the vegetables.

**Table 14.** Vegetables suitable for stuffing

---

*Marrow*
Choose small, young marrows as these will have more flavour and softer skins than large ones. Wash them thoroughly (but do not peel), top and tail and slice into 2″ (5 cm) thick slices. Scoop out and discard the seeds to form hollow rings and then stuff the ring with your chosen filling. Lay on a greased baking sheet, cover with foil and bake for 30–40 minutes until soft (Gas 5/190°C/375°F) removing the foil for the last 10 minutes to crisp the stuffing. Allow two slices per person.

*Beef Tomatoes*
Large beef tomatoes are best for stuffing although smaller ones can be used

if they are firm. Slice the rounded top off the tomato and scoop out the flesh and seeds. (The centres of the tomatoes can be chopped or liquidized and used in place of tinned tomatoes in soup, sauces and casseroles). Fill with your chosen stuffing then put the tops back on to form a lid. Place on a greased baking sheet, cover with foil and bake for 20–25 minutes until soft (Gas 5/190°C/375°F). Allow one per person.

### Courgettes

Choose larger courgettes and wash thoroughly. Top and tail, then cut a 'V' shape out of the top of each courgette to form a hole. Scoop out any seeds with a teaspoon to hollow out the 'V'. (The middle of the courgettes can be used in ratatouille or other vegetable dishes). Stuff the hollow then place the courgettes on a greased baking tray. Cover with foil and bake for 30 minutes until soft (Gas 5/190°C/375°F) removing the foil for the last 10 minutes to crisp the stuffing. Allow two per person.

### Peppers

Choose firm, fresh peppers – either red or green. *Either* cut each pepper in half horizontally, scoop out the seeds and stuff each half *or* cut the top off the pepper (stalk end) scoop out the seeds, stuff the whole pepper and put the top back on to form a lid. Place on a greased baking tray, cover with foil and bake for 30–40 minutes until soft (Gas 5/190°C/375°F) removing foil for the last 10 minutes to crisp stuffing. Allow one per person.

### Mushrooms

Choose large, flat mushrooms. Wash, remove the stalk and put a ball of stuffing on the gills of each mushroom. (The stalks can be used in sauces, soups or other savoury dishes.) Press down lightly. Place on a greased baking tray, cover with foil and bake for 20 minutes until soft (Gas 5/190°C/375°F) removing foil for the last 5 minutes to crisp stuffing. Allow two per person.

### Aubergine

Choose small, young aubergines as these are tastier and have less bitter skins than larger ones. Top and tail, then slice each in half lengthways. Make a deep slit down the centre of each half and scoop out the centre with a teaspoon (the centres can be chopped and used for ratatouille or curry etc). Pack the stuffing into the centre of the aubergine then place the halves on a greased baking tray. Cover with foil and bake for 30–40 minutes until soft (Gas 5/190°C/375°F) removing foil for last 10 minutes to crisp stuffing. One aubergine will serve two people.

### Pumpkin or Squash

Choose small, young vegetables. Wash thoroughly but do not peel, then slice the stalk end off. Scoop out and discard the seeds (unless you want to dry them and remove the husks to make them edible) then hollow out the inside. Fill with stuffing and put the top back on to form a lid. Place on a greased baking tray, cover with foil and bake for 1 hour until soft (Gas 5/190°C/375°F). Cut into thick wedges to serve, keeping the stuffing in place as best you can. Do not eat the skin. One small pumpkin or squash will serve 4–6 people.

**Nutty Stuffing**

A tasty mixture of nuts, rice and vegetables suitable for stuffing marrow, tomatoes, courgettes, peppers, mushrooms, aubergine or pumpkin.

    2 oz (50 g) walnuts, chopped finely
    2 oz (50 g) long grain brown rice, washed
    2 oz (50 g) breadcrumbs
    2 carrots, grated
    2 cloves garlic, crushed
    4 oz (100 g) mushrooms, chopped
    1 onion, chopped finely
    1 tablespoon oil
    1 teaspoon mace powder
    1 teaspoon sage
    2 tablespoons fresh chopped parsley
    1 tablespoon soy sauce
    1 tablespoon tomato purée
    1 teaspoon wholegrain mustard
    3–4 tablespoons stock
    Pepper

*Method*

• Cook the rice according to previous instructions. Drain and rinse.
• Fry the carrot, garlic, mushrooms and onion in the oil until softening.
• Mix the cooked rice with the fried vegetables, nuts, breadcrumbs, mace, sage, parsley, soy sauce, tomato purée, mustard and pepper.
• Add enough stock to form a stiff, moist stuffing.
• This quantity will stuff 8 marrow rings, 4 tomatoes, 8 courgettes, 4 peppers, 8 mushrooms, 1 aubergine or 1 pumpkin.
• Freezes well in plastic containers.

**Rice and Beansprout Stuffing**

A nutritious mixture suitable for stuffing marrow, tomatoes, aubergine or pumpkin.

2 oz (50 g) long-grain brown rice
1 onion, chopped finely
½ red pepper, sliced
1 clove garlic, crushed
1 courgette, chopped finely
2 oz (50 g) mushrooms, chopped
1 tablespoon oil
4 oz (100 g) lentil or mung bean sprouts
1 tablespoon tomato purée
1 teaspoon basil
Pepper
2–3 oz (50–75 g) breadcrumbs

### Method

• Cook the rice according to previous instructions. Drain and rinse.
• Fry the onion, pepper, garlic, courgette and mushrooms in the oil until soft. Stir in the beansprouts, rice, tomato purée, basil and pepper.
• Add enough breadcrumbs to form a stiff stuffing.
• This quantity will stuff 8 marrow rings, 4 tomatoes, 1 aubergine or 1 pumpkin.
• Freezes well in plastic containers.

### Brown Lentil and Apricot Stuffing

A delicious fruity mixture suitable for stuffing marrow, courgettes, peppers, mushrooms, aubergine or pumpkin.

4 oz (100 g) brown lentils, washed thoroughly
2 oz (50 g) dried apricots, chopped
½ stock cube
½ red pepper, finely chopped
1 small onion, finely chopped
1 clove garlic, crushed
Knob margarine
1 tablespoon fresh chopped parsley
½ teaspoon cumin
2 teaspoons soy sauce
3 oz (75 g) breadcrumbs
Pepper

*Method*

- Put the lentils and apricots in a pan with the stock cube. Cover with water, bring to the boil then cover and simmer on a low heat for 30 minutes until the lentils are soft and swollen. (Add more water as necessary and stir regularly to prevent sticking).
- Fry the onion, pepper and garlic in the margarine until softening.
- Mix the lentil purée with the fried vegetables, parsley, cumin, soy sauce and pepper. Add enough breadcrumbs to make a stiff, moist stuffing.
- This quantity will stuff 8 marrow rings, 8 courgettes, 4 peppers, 8 mushrooms, 1 aubergine or 1 pumpkin.
- Freezes well in plastic containers but use within 6 weeks.

## Buckwheat and Sunflower Seed Stuffing

A very savoury mixture with the characteristic flavour of buckwheat. Suitable for stuffing marrow, tomatoes, courgettes, peppers, mushrooms, aubergine or pumpkin.

4 oz (100 g) buckwheat roasted (see p. 85)
or bought ready roasted
1 stock cube
1 teaspoon mixed herbs
1 tablespoon oil
1 stick celery, finely chopped
½ green pepper, finely chopped
2 oz (50 g) mushrooms, chopped
1 onion, finely chopped
2 cloves garlic, crushed
1 tablespoon fresh chopped parsley
1 dessertspoon soy sauce
2 oz (50 g) sunflower seeds
Pepper

*Method*

- Put the buckwheat in a pan with the stock cube and mixed herbs. Cover with water, bring to the boil, cover and simmer on a low heat for 20 minutes until soft and mushy. (Add more water as necessary and stir regularly to prevent sticking).

- Fry the celery, pepper, mushrooms, onion and garlic in the oil until softening.
- Mix the cooked buckwheat with the fried vegetables, parsley, soy sauce, sunflower seeds and pepper to make a stiff stuffing.
- This quantity will stuff 8 marrow rings, 4 tomatoes, 8 courgettes, 4 peppers, 8 mushrooms, 1 aubergine or 1 pumpkin.
- Freezes well in plastic containers.

## Tofu Stuffing

This tasty, nutritious mixture is suitable for stuffing marrow, tomatoes, courgettes, peppers, mushrooms, aubergine or pumpkin.

6 oz (175 g) firm tofu, drained and mashed
6 oz (175 g) breadcrumbs
1 clove garlic, crushed
1 onion, finely chopped
2 sticks celery, finely chopped
2 carrots, finely chopped
Knob margarine
1 tablespoon tomato purée
1 tablespoon soy sauce
1 teaspoon nutmeg
1 teaspoon coriander
1 tablespoon fresh chopped parsley
2–3 tablespoons stock
Pepper

*Method*

- Fry the garlic, onion, celery and carrot in the margarine until soft.
- Mix the fried vegetables with the tofu, breadcrumbs, tomato purée, soy sauce, nutmeg, coriander, parsley and pepper.
- Add enough stock to form a stiff, moist stuffing.
- This quantity will stuff 8 marrow rings, 4 tomatoes, 8 courgettes, 4 peppers, 8 mushrooms, 1 aubergine or 1 pumpkin.
- Can be frozen but the tofu will go slightly chewy.

## Chick Pea and Lemon Stuffing

This sweet tangy stuffing is ideal for stuffing marrow, tomatoes, courgettes, peppers, mushrooms, aubergine or pumpkin.

4 oz (100 g) chick peas
1 tablespoon oil
1 onion, finely chopped
1 clove garlic, crushed
2 carrots, grated
1 small cooking apple, peeled, cored and grated
1 tablespoon fresh chopped parsley
1 teaspoon sage
1 teaspoon coriander
1 tablespoon tomato purée
1 teaspoon yeast extract
2 oz (50 g) breadcrumbs
Rind 1 small lemon
Pepper

### *Method*

• Presoak and cook the chick peas. Drain and reserve liquid.
• Fry the onion, garlic, carrots and apple in the oil until soft.
• Mash or liquidize the chick peas to a stiff paste with 4 tablespoons of the chickpea liquid.
• Mix the chick pea paste with the fried vegetables, parsley, sage, coriander, tomato purée, yeast extract, lemon rind and breadcrumbs to form a stiff, moist stuffing.
• This quantity will stuff 8 marrow rings, 4 tomatoes, 8 courgettes, 4 peppers, 8 mushrooms, 1 aubergine or 1 pumpkin.
• Freezes well in plastic containers.

PIES / FLANS
COBBLERS
CRUMBLES

## Wholemeal Shortcrust

Some people have such a problem with shortcrust pastry that they eventually give up. With a bit of perseverance and the following tips, you will be able to make delicious crisp, melt-in-the-mouth pastry that is not only nutritionally superior to white but contains valuable fibre, an aid in the control of appetite.

There are two important rules for pastry-making:

**1** *Don't be afraid of it!* Wholemeal flour contains all the bran from the wheat which acts as a natural shortening agent. Therefore if you overhandle the pastry or have to roll it more than once it will not go tough like white pastry. Wholemeal pastry can be turned over and floured on both sides and rolled sideways with no detrimental effect — if you did this to white pastry it would taste like cardboard!

**2** *Make the pastry very wet.* Wholemeal flour soaks up a lot more water than white so you must adjust accordingly. If the pastry is nice and wet it will be more pliable and easy to roll out, eliminating the need to chill it first or roll between sheets of greaseproof. It is far better to have it too wet than too dry. If it is dry the pastry will be crumbly and impossible to roll. If it is too wet, just knead in a bit more flour, it won't hurt the pastry at all.

### Recipe

*Makes 8 oz (225 g)*

8 oz (225 g) 100% wholemeal flour
4 oz (100 g) cold vegan margarine
Cold water to mix

- Rub the margarine into the flour with your fingertips until the mixture looks like breadcrumbs. *Do not overrub* or the pastry will be too short (if in doubt, underrub).
- Add the cold water, a *teaspoonful at a time* mixing in with a knife until a *soft, wet dough* is formed. Knead gently with *one hand* until it leaves the sides of the bowl clean.
- Turn onto a *very well floured* board and roll the pastry in flour to stop it sticking to your hands (if it is too wet, knead in some more flour).
- Roll out gently moving the pastry about *all the time* to ensure it hasn't stuck. If it is sticking turn it over to flour both sides. Keep the rolling pin well floured.
- Roll out as thinly as you can then use as required.
- Wholemeal pastry can be frozen and is often easier to handle when it has been. Use in 3–4 months.


**Nutty Wholemeal Shortcrust**

As nuts contain fat you will probably need less water in this pastry than for regular shortcrust. Nutty pastry can be very short so I would advise chilling prior to use for easier handling. This pastry is delicious for sweet and savoury dishes giving added nutritive value and flavour. Any nuts can be used but it is better to stick to less fatty ones such as hazels, cashews or almonds.


*Recipe*

*Makes 8 oz (225 g)*

8 oz (225 g) 100% wholemeal flour
2 oz (50 g) finely ground nuts
4 oz (100 g) cold vegan margarine
Cold water to mix.

- Rub the margarine into the flour with your fingertips until the mixture looks like breadcrumbs (as for shortcrust).
- Stir in the nuts then add the water a *teaspoonful at a time*

until a *soft, wet dough* is formed (as for shortcrust). Less water will probably be required.

• Knead gently with one hand to form a soft ball and chill for 30 minutes prior to use.

• Roll and use as for shortcrust.

• Freezes well but does not keep so well as shortcrust owing to the higher fat content. Use within 2 months.

## Wholemeal Flaky Pastry

This pastry does take a bit of time to make but is well worth the effort as ready-made vegan puff or flaky pastry is not readily available.

Flaky pastry has a very high fat content and can be difficult to handle as a result. The golden rule is to keep everything as *cool as possible* and chill the pastry in between rollings if it is becoming sticky.

As long as you follow the instructions below implicitly you will be pleasantly surprised at how easy it is! I would not recommend beginners to attempt this pastry until they have perfected their wholemeal shortcrust.

This pastry can be used for sweet and savoury pies, vegan 'sausage' rolls and sweet slices.

### *Recipe*

*Makes 8 oz (225 g)*

> 8 oz (225 g) 100% wholemeal flour
> 6 oz (175 g) cold margarine (from fridge)
> 1 teaspoon lemon juice
> ¼ pint (150 ml) cold water

• Rub 2 oz (50 g) of the margarine into the flour until the mixture resembles breadcrumbs.

• Add the lemon juice and enough cold water to make a *soft, wet dough* (similar to shortcrust). Knead gently with *one hand* until it leaves the sides of the bowl clean.

• Roll out on a *very well floured board* to an oblong approximately 6″ × 12″ (15 × 30 cm). (Try to keep a good oblong shape as this will help greatly in the later stages). See Fig.2.

• Divide the remaining margarine into four equal 1 oz (25 g) portions. Chop the first portion into *small flakes* and

140

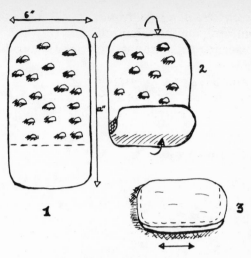

**Figure 2**

dot these all over the *top two-thirds* of the pastry oblong you have rolled out.

• Fold the *bottom third* of the pastry *up* over the middle third to cover the margarine flakes. Then fold the *top third down* over this. Press the edges with your thumbs to seal the margarine in.

• Give the pastry a *quarter turn* to the left so the sealed edge is on *your left*. Roll out again gently to an oblong as above taking care not to break any air bubbles that appear under the surface of the dough (these are caused by the triple folding process and contribute to the flakiness of the finished pastry).

• Dot the next 1 oz (25 g) of margarine on the top two-thirds of the oblong. Fold as above, seal and give another quarter-turn.

• Repeat the proces *two more times* to use up all the margarine, then roll and fold *twice* more without using any margarine. Chill the dough in between rollings if it is becoming too sticky.

• Allow the pastry to rest in the fridge for 30 minutes before using.

• When you come to use the pastry, roll it out fairly thickly approx ½"/1 cm and cut the edges with a sharp knife after shaping your pie. This gives a flakier texture and makes the pastry 'puff up' better. 'Knocking up' the cut edges with the back of a knife will also help give a flakier appearance.

• Wholemeal flaky pastry freezes well. Use in 3–4 months. As this pastry takes longer to make it is worth while making more than one batch and freezing it.

## Brazil Nut and Mushroom Pie

A delicious change from a nut roast, this dish makes a very impressive dinner party main course. It is very rich and will easily serve 6 people.

6 oz (175 g) wholemeal shortcrust pastry
1 onion, chopped finely
1 clove garlic, crushed
4 oz (100 g) mushrooms, sliced
½ oz (12 g) margarine
½ oz (12 g) flour
¼ pint (150 ml) stock
1 teaspoon yeast extract
1 tablespoon tomato purée
6 oz (175 g) brazil nuts, finely chopped or ground
3 oz (75 g) wholemeal breadcrumbs
Rind and juice 1 small lemon
1 tablespoon fresh chopped parsley
1 teaspoon sage
½ teaspoon mace
Pepper
Soya milk to glaze

*Method*

Set oven to Gas 6/200°C/400°F.

• Fry the onion, garlic and mushrooms in the margarine until softening.
• Stir in the flour and cook for a few seconds.
• *Remove from heat* and stir in the stock gradually to avoid lumps. Add the yeast extract and tomato purée.
• Return to the heat and stir until the sauce thickens and is bubbling.
• Mix the sauce with the nuts, breadcrumbs, lemon rind and juice, parsley, sage, mace and pepper to form a stiffish mixture. Allow to cool slightly.
• Make the pastry according to the instructions on page 138, using 6 oz (175 g) flour to 3 oz (75 g) margarine.

- Roll out two-thirds of the pastry on a well floured board and use it to line an 8″ (20 cm) pie dish or flan ring.
- Spread the nut mixture in the pastry case and brush the edges of the pastry with soya milk.
- Roll out the remaining pastry to fit the top of the pie, cover the filling and seal the edges well. Trim and flute the edges.
- Brush with soya milk, make a slit in the top and bake for 25–30 minutes until the pastry is golden brown.
- Serve hot or cold with jacket potatoes, miso sauce and green vegetables or salad.
- Freeze the pie raw and bake from frozen.

## Adzuki and Black-Eye Pie

This mildly spiced pie can be served hot as a main course or cold for lunch boxes and picnics. Any beans may be used if adzukis and black-eyes are not available.

6 oz (175 g) shortcrust pastry
6 oz (175 g) adzuki and black-eyed beans (mixed)
Knob margarine
1 onion, chopped
1 knob fresh ginger, peeled and grated
2 cloves garlic, crushed
$\frac{1}{2}$ red pepper, sliced
4 oz (100 g) mushrooms, sliced
Small tin tomatoes, chopped
1 tablespoon tomato purée
2 teaspoons coriander
2 teaspoons cumin
1 teaspoon cardamom powder
$\frac{1}{2}$ teaspoon nutmeg
pepper
Soya milk to glaze

*Method*

Set oven to Gas 6/200°C/400°F.

- Presoak and cook the beans. Drain and reserve the liquid.
- Melt the margarine and fry the onion, ginger, garlic, pepper and mushrooms for a few minutes until soft.
- Add the chopped tomatoes, tomato purée, spices and pepper. Bring to the boil and simmer for 5 minutes until thick (it must

143

not be too runny or the pastry will go soggy).

• Add the cooked beans, stir well and allow to cool while you make the pastry.

• Make the pastry as described on page 138. Use 6 oz (175 g) flour and 3 oz (75 g) margarine. Roll out two-thirds of it and line an 8″ (20 cm) pie dish or flan ring.

• Pile the bean filling into the pastry case. Brush the edges of the pastry with soya milk.

• Roll out the remaining pastry to make a lid for the pie, lay on top and press lightly to seal the edges. Trim the edges and flute to decorate. Make a hole in the top of the pie. Brush with soya milk.

• Bake for 20–30 minutes until the pastry is well browned.

• Serve hot with potatoes and green vegetables or cold as part of a buffet meal.

• Freeze uncooked and bake from frozen.


### Vegetable and Chick Pea Pie

A tasty nutritious pie that makes the most of summer vegetables. (Serves 4–6).

6 oz (175 g) shortcrust pastry
4 oz (100 g) chick peas
1 onion, chopped
2 cloves garlic, crushed
½ red pepper, sliced
4 oz (100 g) mushrooms, sliced
4 courgettes, sliced
2 sticks celery, chopped
1 tablespoon olive oil
8 oz (225 g) fresh or frozen spinach, finely chopped
1 small tin tomatoes, chopped
2 tablespoons tomato purée
2 teaspoons nutmeg
1 teaspoon marjoram
1 tablespoon fresh chopped parsley
Pepper
Soya milk to glaze


*Method*

Set oven to Gas 6/200°C/400°F.

144

- Presoak and cook the chick peas. Drain and reserve liquid.
- Fry the onion, garlic, pepper, mushrooms, courgettes and celery in the oil until softening. Add the spinach and fry for one minute more.
- Add the tomatoes, tomato purée, nutmeg, marjoram, parsley and pepper and simmer for 5 minutes until the vegetables are cooked.
- Stir in the chick peas and cool slightly
- Make the pastry according to the instructions on page 138. Use 6 oz (175 g) flour with 3 oz (75 g) margarine. Roll out two thirds of it on a well floured board to fit an 8" (20 cm) pie dish or flan ring.
- Pile the filling into the pastry case and brush the edges with soya milk.
- Roll out the remaining pastry to fit the top of the pie, lay over the vegetables and seal the edges. Trim the edges and flute if desired.
- Make a slit in the pie, brush with soya milk and bake for 25–30 minutes until the pastry is golden.
- Serve hot with miso sauce or tomato sauce, potatoes and salad.
- Freeze raw and bake from frozen.

**Flaky Smoked Tofu and Vegetable Pie**

This unusual mixture of flavours and textures is particularly popular for dinner parties but equally good as a family meal.

  4 oz (100 g) flaky pastry (see p. 140)
  4 oz (100 g) smoked tofu, drained and cut into cubes
  2 courgettes, sliced
  4 oz (100 g) cauliflower florets, broken into small pieces
  2 carrots, chopped finely
  1 onion, chopped finely
  1 clove garlic, crushed
  ½ red pepper, sliced
  2 oz (50 g) mushrooms, sliced
  1 oz (25 g) margarine
  1 oz (25 g) wholemeal flour
  ½ pint (275 ml) soya milk
  1 stock cube
  1 tablespoon fresh chopped parsley

$\frac{1}{2}$ teaspoon mace
1 teaspoon yeast extract
Pepper
Soya milk to glaze

## *Method*

Set oven to Gas 7/220°C/425°F.
Grease a 2 pint (1 litre) ovenproof dish.

- Make the flaky pastry. Wrap and chill for 30 minutes.
- Fry the courgettes, cauliflower, carrots, onion, garlic, pepper and mushrooms in the margarine for a few minutes.
- Add the flour, stir in and cook for *one minute*.
- *Remove from heat* and add the soya milk gradually, stirring, to form a smooth sauce around the vegetables. Return to heat and stir continuously until the sauce has thickened and is bubbling.
- Add the stock cube, parsley, yeast extract, mace and pepper and stir over a low heat until mixed thoroughly.
- Stir in the tofu cubes and pile into the prepared dish.
- Roll the flaky pastry out on a well floured board to fit the top of the dish. Lay it over the vegetables and trim to fit.
- Make a hole in the top of the pastry, brush with soya milk and bake for 20 minutes until the pastry is well risen and brown.
- Serve with vegetables or salad.
- Freeze the pie raw, and bake from frozen.

*Note:* If smoked tofu is not available use plain tofu and sprinkle it with about one tablespoon soy sauce before adding to the sauce.

## Black-eyed Bean and Vegetable Roll

This is an interesting variation on the traditional pie and is particularly nice cold with salad or as part of a buffet meal. Serve hot with miso sauce or tomato sauce.

8 oz (225 g) wholemeal shortcrust pastry
4 oz (100 g) black-eyed beans
1 tablespoon oil
1 onion, chopped
2 cloves garlic, crushed

1 courgette, chopped
1 stick celery, sliced
2 oz (50 g) mushrooms, sliced
2 carrots, diced finely
1 tablespoon frozen or tinned corn
1 tablespoon fresh chopped parsley
1 teaspoon tarragon
1 tablespoon tomato purée
1 teaspoon yeast extract
Pepper
Soya milk to glaze

## Method

Set oven to Gas 6/200°C/400°F.

- Presoak and cook the beans. Drain and reserve liquid.
- Fry the onion, garlic, courgette, celery, mushrooms and carrots in the oil until softening.
- Add the cooked beans, parsley, tarragon, tomato purée and yeast extract. Season and moisten with 4–5 tablespoonfuls of the bean water. Cook on a low heat for a few more minutes until moist and thickened. Allow to cool.
- Make the pastry. Roll out quite thickly on a well floured board to an oblong approximately 12″ × 8″ (30 × 20 cm).
- Spread the cooled bean mixture over the pastry leaving a 1″ (2.5 cm) border around the edges. (*Note: the filling must be cool or the pastry will go soggy and be impossible to roll*)
- Roll the pastry up over the filling like a swiss roll with the shorter side of the oblong facing you. Push any loose filling back in.
- Lay the roll on a baking tray, mark the top with slits and brush with soya milk.
- Bake for 25–30 minutes until the pastry is well browned. Serve hot with miso sauce, potatoes and green vegetables or cold in picnics.
- Freeze the roll unbaked and bake from frozen.

## Cashew and Vegetable Plait

This interesting dish makes a very impressive dinner party centrepiece. It takes a while to prepare but is well worth the effort. The filling can be prepared in advance to save time on

147

the day it is to be served. (Serves 4–6).

8 oz (225 g) shortcrust pastry
1 oz (25 g) margarine
1 onion, finely chopped
2 oz (50 g) mushrooms, sliced
1 clove garlic, crushed
½ green pepper, sliced
4 oz (100 g) cauliflower florets, broken into small pieces
4 oz (100 g) mangetout, chopped
2 courgettes, chopped finely
4 oz (100 g) fennel, chopped finely
1 heaped tablespoon flour
¼ pint (150 ml) soya milk
1 teaspoon stock concentrate
2 tablespoons fresh chopped parsley
1 teaspoon coriander
1 teaspoon miso
4 oz (100 g) cashew nuts
Pepper
Soya milk to glaze

*Method*

Set oven to Gas 6/200°C/400°F.

• *Prepare filling first:* fry the onion, mushrooms, garlic, pepper, cauliflower, mangetout, courgettes and fennel in the margarine until softening. Cover and leave to 'sweat' for 5 minutes.
• Stir in the flour and cook for one minute.
• *Remove from heat* and stir in the soya milk gradually, stirring continuously to form a thick sauce.
• Return to heat and cook for one minute until the mixture is thick. Stir in the stock concentrate, parsley, coriander, miso, cashews and pepper. Leave to cool.
• Make the pastry (Fig. 3). Roll out on a well floured board to a 12″ × 12″ (30 × 30 cm) square. Put the square onto a baking tray.
• Lay the cooled filling down the central 4″ (10 cm) of the square and press with the hands to firm slightly. Cut a 1″ (2.5 cm) deep flap in the pastry at the top and bottom of the filling and fold up over each end. Discard the surplus pastry on either side of the flaps.

148

- Cut the pastry on either side of the filling into ten 1″ (2.5 cm) thick strips leaving 1″ (2.5 cm) of the pastry closest to the filling uncut.
- Starting at the top, fold the strips over the filling, taking one from either side to form a plaited effect. Keep them close together so the filling is covered and press together lightly in the middle.
- Continue down all the strips until the whole filling is covered.
- Brush with soya milk and bake for 20–25 minutes until the pastry is golden.
- Serve hot with steamed vegetables and new potatoes.
- Freeze unbaked and cook from frozen.

*Variations:* if you are feeling adventurous and have the time, this plait is delicious made with 8 oz (225 g) flaky pastry. The same filling can be used to fill a normal pie in an 8″ (20 cm) pie dish using 6 oz (175 g) shortcrust pastry.

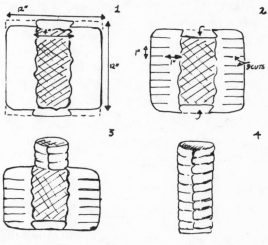

**Figure 3**

## Tofu Quiche

A low calorie, no cholesterol, vegan version of a traditional favourite. Serve hot or cold. (Serves 4–6).

4 oz (100 g) wholemeal shortcrust pastry (half recipe quantities page 138)

149

8 oz (225 g) *firm* tofu
Knob margarine
1 large onion, sliced
4 oz (100 g) mushrooms, sliced
1 clove garlic, crushed
½ red pepper, sliced
1 heaped tablespoon sweetcorn
1 tablespoon tomato purée
1 tablespoon soy sauce
1 teaspoon mixed herbs
Black pepper
1 tablespoon sesame seeds

## Method

Set the oven to Gas 6/200°C/400°F.

- Make the pastry. Roll out to fit on an 8″ (20 cm) pie dish or flan ring. Trim off the edges.
- Fry the onion, garlic, mushrooms, pepper and corn in the margarine for a few minutes. Cool slightly.
- Mash or liquidize the tofu with some of the water in the pack until it is soft and creamy.
- Add the fried vegetables and all the other ingredients except sesame seeds. Season well. (The mixture should not be too wet or the tofu will not set properly when cooked. Add some wholemeal breadcrumbs if you have made it too sloppy).
- Pour the tofu mixture into the prepared flan case and sprinkle sesame seeds on top.
- Bake for 30–40 minutes until the flan is set and golden brown.
- Serve with salad and new potatoes.
- Not suitable for freezing as the tofu goes very chewy.

## Lentil and Pepper Flan

This colourful flan is very popular cold at picnics but is equally delicious hot with vegetables. (Serves 4–6).

4 oz (100 g) shortcrust pastry (half the recipe quantities on page 138)
6 oz (175 g) red lentils, washed thoroughly

1 vegetable stock cube
1 onion, chopped
1 clove garlic, crushed
Knob margarine
½ red and ½ green pepper, sliced
1 tablespoon tomato purée
1 teaspoon yeast extract
½ teaspoon nutmeg
1 teaspoon savory
1 tablespoon fresh chopped parsley
Black pepper

## *Method*

Set oven to Gas 6/200°C/400°F.

• Make the pastry. Roll out on a well floured board and use to line an 8″ (20 cm) pie dish or flan ring. Trim edges.
• Put the lentils in a pan with the stock cube and enough water to cover. Bring to the boil, skim off any froth, then simmer for 20 minutes until the lentils are soft and can be beaten to a smooth puree. (More water may need to be added during cooking but try not to make the mixture too wet).
• Fry the onion and garlic in the margarine until softening and add to the lentil puree with the chopped peppers, tomato puree, yeast extract, nutmeg, savory, parsley and pepper. Mix thoroughly.
• Pour into the prepared pastry case and bake for 30 minutes until brown and the lentils are firm.
• Serve hot with salad or cold with a picnic meal. Will keep 3–4 days in an airtight container if refrigerated.
• Freeze unbaked, thaw and bake as normal.

## Green Pea, Mushroom and Sweetcorn Flan

A lovely colourful vegan flan which is delicious hot or cold.

4 oz (100 g) shortcrust pastry (see p. 138)
6 oz (175 g) green split peas, washed thoroughly
1 stock cube
1 bay leaf
1 teaspoon thyme
1 onion, chopped

2 cloves garlic, crushed
4 oz (100 g) mushrooms, sliced
4 oz (100 g) frozen or tinned sweetcorn
Knob margarine
1 tablespoon fresh chopped parsley
1 teaspoon ground mace
Rind ½ a lemon
1 teaspoon yeast extract
Pepper

*Method*

Set oven to Gas 6/200°C/400°F.

• Put the split peas, stock cube, bay leaf and thyme in a pan, cover with water and bring to the boil. Cover and simmer on a low heat for 40 minutes until the peas are soft enough to be beaten to a smooth puree. (Add more water during cooking as necessary and stir regularly). Remove bay leaf.

• Fry the onion, garlic, mushrooms and corn in the margarine until softening. Add to the pea puree with the parsley, mace, lemon rind, yeast extract and pepper. Allow to cool slightly.

• Make the pastry. Roll out on a well floured board and line an 8″ (20 cm) pie dish or flan ring. Trim edges.

• Put the pea filling in the pastry case and smooth over.

• Bake for 30 minutes until well browned and the filling is set. Serve hot or cold with salad and potatoes.

• Keeps 4–5 days in an airtight container in the fridge.

• Freeze raw, thaw and bake.

**Bean and Mushroom Flan**

A very savoury flan which is equally good hot or cold. Any white beans may be used. (Serves 4–6).

4 oz (100 g) shortcrust pastry (see p. 138)
6 oz (175 g) white beans (e.g. haricot, butter, blackeyes)
1 onion, finely chopped
4 oz (100 g) mushrooms, sliced
1 clove garlic, crushed
Knob margarine
1 tablespoon fresh chopped parsley

1 tablespoon tomato purée
Rind 1 small lemon
1 teaspoon yeast extract
1 teaspoon wholegrain mustard
1 teaspoon sage
Pepper

## Method

Set oven to Gas 6/200°C/400°F.

- Presoak and cook the beans. Drain and reserve liquid.
- Make the pastry. Roll out and use to line an 8″ (20 cm) pie plate or flan ring. Trim to fit.
- Fry the onion, garlic and mushrooms in the margarine until softening.
- Liquidize or mash the beans to a smooth puree with 2 tablespoons cooking water. Add the fried vegetables, parsley, tomato purée, lemon rind, yeast extract, mustard, sage and pepper.
- Pile into the prepared flan case and smooth over. Bake for 30 minutes until the pastry is golden and the filling set.
- Serve hot with new potatoes and salad or cold in picnics.
- Freeze unbaked and bake from frozen.

## Hazelnut and Tofu Flan

This tasty, nutritious flan is equally delicious hot or cold. It is quite rich so will probably serve 6–8 people.

4 oz (100 g) shortcrust pastry
Knob margarine
1 onion, finely chopped
1 clove garlic, crushed
10 oz (175 g) *firm* tofu, drained
3 oz (75 g) ground hazelnuts
1 tablespoon soy sauce
1 tablespoon fresh chopped parsley
1 teaspoon sage
$\frac{1}{2}$ teaspoon nutmeg
1 tablespoon sunflower seeds
Pepper

153

## Method

Set the oven to Gas 6/200°C/400°F.

- Make the pastry. Roll out to line an 8″ (20 cm) pie dish or flan ring. Trim and put to one side.
- Fry the onion and garlic in the margarine until browning.
- Put the tofu in a liquidizer with the soy sauce and 3 tablespoons water. Whizz to form a smooth cream.
- Mix the tofu cream with the fried onions, nuts, parsley, sage, nutmeg and pepper.
- Pile into the prepared pastry case and smooth over. Sprinkle the sunflower seeds on top.
- Bake for 20–25 minutes until the tofu is firm and brown and the pastry cooked.
- Serve hot with potatoes and a salad or cold in picnics.
- Not suitable for freezing.

## an and Vegetable Slices

Very popular with children, these nutritious fingers are excellent for packed lunches or parties. They can also be served hot as a main course with miso sauce. (Serves 12).

8 oz (225 g) shortcrust pastry
4 oz (100 g) red kidney beans
Knob margarine
1 onion, chopped
1 carrot, chopped
2 oz (50 g) mushrooms, chopped
$\frac{1}{2}$ a green pepper, chopped
Small piece of swede, chopped
1 teaspoon marjoram
1 teaspoon coriander
1 teaspoon yeast extract/miso
Black pepper
Soya milk to glaze

## Method

Set oven to Gas 7/220°C/425°F.
Lightly grease a 9″ × 12″ (23 × 30 cm) swiss roll tin or similar baking tray.

- Presoak and cook the beans as described. Drain and reserve the liquid.
- Fry the onion, carrot, mushrooms, pepper and swede in the margarine until softening.
- Put the fried vegetables, marjoram, coriander, yeast extract/miso and cooked beans in a liquidizer and blend until smooth, adding some bean water if necessary. (The mixture should not be too wet). Season well with pepper.
- Make the pastry. Divide in half.
- Roll out one half to an oblong to fit the prepared swiss roll tin and press lightly to line the base of the tin.
- Spread the bean mixture evenly over the pastry then roll the other piece of pastry to an oblong that will cover the mixture. Place on top and press lightly.
- Prick all over with a fork and brush with soya milk.
- Bake for 20 minutes until the pastry is golden. Cool slightly then slice into 12 bars. When cold remove from tin and store in the fridge until required.
- These slices are better frozen cooked and stored in bags or plastic boxes.

*Variation:* Add 2 teaspoons curry powder instead of the marjoram for a lightly curried mixture.


### Lentil and Fennel Slices

The characteristic flavour of fennel seems to go particularly well with lentils and these slices are delicious hot or cold as a main course or a picnic item. (Makes 12 slices).

8 oz (225 g) shortcrust pastry
6 oz (175 g) red lentils, washed thoroughly
1 stock cube
12 oz (350 g) fennel, chopped finely (leaves and white parts)
1 onion, finely chopped
2 cloves garlic, crushed
Knob margarine
4 oz (100 g) breadcrumbs
2 tablespoons fresh chopped parsley
1 tablespoon tomato purée
1 teaspoon yeast extract
1 teaspoon mace

Pepper
Soya milk to glaze

## *Method*

Set oven to Gas 6/200°C/400°F.

• Put the lentils in a pan with the stock cube and chopped fennel. Cover with water and bring to the boil. Cover and simmer on a low heat for 15–20 minutes until the lentils are cooked and mushy. Stir occasionally to prevent sticking and add more water as necessary. Try not to make the mixture too wet.

• Fry the onion and garlic in the margarine until soft then add to the lentil purée with the breadcrumbs, parsley, tomato purée, yeast extract, mace and pepper. Stir well and cool slightly.

• Make the pastry. Divide in half. Roll one half out to an oblong that will fit a 9″ × 12″ (23 × 30 cm) swiss roll tin or similar baking tray.

• Spread the lentil mixture on top of the pastry. Roll the remaining pastry out to fit the top of the lentils and press down lightly.

• Prick the pastry all over with a fork, brush with soya milk and bake for 20–25 minutes until the pastry is golden.

• Slice into 12 bars while warm and serve hot with miso gravy (see page 240) and vegetables or cold as a picnic item.

• Freeze the slice raw and bake from frozen.


## Curry Pasties

These spicy pasties are equally nice hot as a main course or cold for picnics. The recipe makes 4 large pasties but could be used to make 8 small ones suitable for lunch boxes if preferred.

8 oz (225 g) shortcrust pastry
1 lb (450 g) diced root vegetables e.g. carrot, potato, celeriac, parsnip, swede, beetroot etc.
1 onion, chopped
2 cloves garlic, crushed
1 tablespoon oil
½ teaspoon cayenne pepper

1 teaspoon curry powder
1 teaspoon wholegrain mustard
2 teaspoons pickle
1 teaspoon turmeric
1 teaspoon cumin
1 teaspoon coriander
¼ pint (150 ml) stock
Soya milk to glaze

## Method

Set oven to Gas 6/200°C/400°F.

• *Make the filling first:* fry the vegetables, onion and garlic in the oil for a few minutes.

• Add the cayenne, curry powder, mustard, pickle, turmeric, cumin and coriander and fry for one minute.

• Add the stock, cover and simmer for 30 minutes stirring occasionally until the vegetables are cooked and all the liquid has been absorbed. Allow to cool.

• Make the pastry. Divide into 4 evenly sized balls.

• Roll each ball into a circle on a well floured board. Divide the filling equally between the 4 circles and place on one half of the pastry. (*The filling must be cool or the pastry will go soggy*).

• Brush the edges of each circle with soya milk then fold the pastry over the filling to form a pasty. Press edges together to seal and trim with a knife. Flute edges with the fingers.

• Make a slit in the top of each pasty, brush with soya milk and place on a baking tray.

• Bake for 25–30 minutes until the pastry is well browned. Serve hot with salad and potatoes or cold for picnics.

• Using 6 oz (175 g) of shortcrust pastry, the same filling can be used to make a large pie in an 8″ (20 cm) pie dish or flan ring.

• To freeze – do not make a slit in the top of the pasties and open freeze, uncooked, on trays. Pack into bags or boxes when frozen. Cook from frozen making a slit in the top before baking.

*Note:* As the pasties contain only wheat protein in the pastry they need to be served with nuts or pulses in order to achieve complementarity. This is easily done by serving with a nut or bean salad or by having a dessert that contains nuts or tofu for example.

## Spicy Bean Shepherds Pie

A mildly spiced bean base and a creamy potato topping with crunchy sunflower seeds makes this an ideal family dish. The base doubles up as a casserole if more stock is added and the potato top omitted from the recipe.

6 oz (175 g) beans (e.g. haricot, black-eye, adzuki, kidney)
2 lb (900 g) potatoes, boiled and mashed with soya milk, margarine and black pepper
1 tablespoon oil
Piece fresh ginger, peeled and grated
2 cloves garlic, crushed
1 large onion, chopped
1 bulb fennel, chopped
4 oz (100 g) mushrooms, sliced
½ red pepper, sliced
Medium tin tomatoes, liquidized or chopped
1 tablespoon tomato purée
1 teaspoon mace
2 teaspoons cumin
2 teaspoons coriander
½ teaspoon cayenne pepper
1 teaspoon wholegrain mustard
1 tablespoon pickle/chutney
1 tablespoon soy sauce
Black pepper
2 tablespoons sunflower seeds

### Method

Set oven to Gas 5/190°C/375°F.
Grease a 3 pint (1½ litre) ovenproof dish or baking tin.

• Presoak and cook the beans. Drain and reserve liquid.
• Fry the ginger, garlic, onion, fennel, mushrooms and pepper in the oil for a few minutes until softening.
• Add the tomatoes, tomato purée, spices, mustard, chutney and soy sauce. Season well with pepper.
• Bring to the boil and simmer for 5 minutes stirring occasionally until the vegetables are cooked and the liquid has thickened.

- Add the cooked beans and cook for another 2 minutes, stirring.
- Pour the bean mixture into the prepared dish and smooth over. Spread the mashed potato on top and fork up to make it look attractive.
- Sprinkle the sunflower seeds on top and bake for 30 minutes until the potato and seeds are brown and crispy.
- Serve with green vegetables or salad.
- Freeze uncooked, thaw and bake as above.

*Note:* I normally leave the skins on potatoes even for mashing. This is not only better nutritionally but gives a nicer flavour and texture.

### Lentil Shepherd's Pie

A very savoury mixture of green lentils and vegetables topped with creamy potato and crunchy sunflower seeds. Ideal for family meals.

2 lb (900 g) potatoes, boiled and mashed with margarine, pepper and soya milk.
1 onion, chopped
2 cloves garlic, crushed
2 large carrots, chopped
2 sticks celery, sliced
1 tablespoon oil
8 oz (225 g) green lentils, washed thoroughly
1¼ pints (650 ml) stock
1 tablespoon tomato purée
1 teaspoon savory
1 teaspoon marjoram
1 teaspoon cumin
1 teaspoon coriander
Black pepper
2 teaspoons miso
2 oz (50 g) sunflower seeds

*Method*
Set oven to Gas 5/190′C/375°F.
Grease a 2 pint (1 litre) ovenproof dish.

- Fry the onion, garlic, carrot and celery in the oil for a few minutes until softening.

159

- Add the lentils, stock, tomato purée, savory, marjoram, cumin, coriander and pepper.
- Bring to the boil, cover and simmer on a low heat for about 30 minutes until the lentils are swollen and soft and all the liquid has been absorbed.
- Cool slightly then stir in the miso. Pile into the prepared dish and smooth over.
- Spread the mashed potato on top of the lentils and fork up to make it look attractive. Sprinkle the sunflower seeds on top and bake for 30 minutes until golden brown and crispy.
- Serve with green vegetables or salad.
- Freeze uncooked, thaw and bake as above.

*Note:* I normally leave the skins on the potatoes even for mashing. This is not only better nutritionally but gives a nicer flavour and texture.

### Split Pea and Walnut Shepherd's Pie

This filling nutritious dish tastes surprisingly 'meaty' — a good one to try on non-vegan friends.

8 oz (225 g) green split peas, washed thoroughly
1 stock cube
2 teaspoons savory
2 bay leaves
3 oz (75 g) roughly chopped walnuts
2 onions, chopped
4 oz (100 g) mushrooms, sliced
2 cloves garlic, crushed
1 tablespoon oil
2 teaspoons miso
1 tablespoon soy-sauce
Pepper
2 lb (900 g) potatoes, boiled and mashed with margarine, pepper, soya milk and 2 tablespoons fresh chopped parsley.

### Method

Set oven to Gas 5/190°C/375°F.
Grease a 2 pint (1 litre) ovenproof dish.

- Put the split peas, stock cube, savory and bayleaves in a

pan. Cover with water, bring to the boil and simmer for about 45 minutes until the split peas are soft and mushy and can be beaten to a puree. Stir regularly during cooking and add more water as necessary if the peas are going dry. (Try not to make the mixture too wet though).

• Remove the bayleaves and beat in the miso, soy sauce and pepper.

• Fry the onions, mushrooms and garlic in the oil until softening. Add to the split peas with the walnuts and stir well.

• Pile into the prepared dish and smooth over.

• Spread the mashed potato on top and fork up to make it look attractive. Bake for 30 minutes until golden brown and crispy.

• Serve with green vegetables or salad.

• Freeze uncooked, thaw and bake as above.

*Note:* I normally leave the skins on the potatoes even for mashing. This is not only better nutritionally but gives a nicer flavour and texture.


## Beany Ratatouille Shepherd's Pie

A delicious and interesting way to make use of summer vegetables like courgettes and aubergines. A popular family meal.

    4 oz (100 g) black-eyed beans
    1 large aubergine, chopped
    4 courgettes, sliced
    1 onion, chopped
    2 cloves garlic, crushed
    1 red pepper, sliced
    4 oz (100 g) mushrooms, sliced
    2 tablespoons olive oil
    Medium tin tomatoes, chopped
    2 tablespoons tomato purée
    2 teaspoons basil
    Pepper
    2 tablespoons sesame seeds
    2 lb (900 g) potatoes, boiled and mashed with margarine, pepper, soya milk and 2 tablespoons fresh chopped parsley.

*Method*

Set oven to Gas 5/190°C/375°F.
Grease a 3 pint (1½ litre) ovenproof dish.

- Presoak and cook the beans. Drain and reserve liquid.
- Fry the aubergine, courgettes, onion, garlic, pepper and mushrooms in the oil for a few minutes. Cover and allow to 'sweat' for 5 minutes.
- Add the tomatoes, tomato purée, basil and pepper. Bring to the boil, cover and simmer for 10–15 minutes until the vegetables are soft and the liquid thickened.
- Stir in the cooked beans and pile into the prepared dish. Smooth over.
- Spread the mashed potato on top and fork up to make it look attractive. Sprinkle the sesame seeds on top.
- Bake for 30 minutes until brown and crispy. Serve with vegetables or salad.
- Freeze uncooked, thaw and bake as above.

*Note:* I normally leave the skins on the potatoes even for mashing. This is not only better nutritionally but gives a nicer flavour and texture.


**Mushroom, Cashew and Lentil Pie**

This tasty pie is very popular with children as mashed potato is used for the base which they seem to enjoy! Very quick and easy to prepare.

1½ lb (675 g) potatoes, boiled and mashed with a knob of margarine, pepper and soya milk
4 oz (100 g) red lentils, washed thoroughly
1 stock cube
1 teaspoon savory
4 oz (100 g) cashew nuts
1 onion, finely chopped
2 cloves garlic, crushed
12 oz (350 g) mushrooms, sliced
Knob margarine
2 tablespoons fresh chopped parsley
1 teaspoon nutmeg
Pepper

*Method*

Set oven to Gas 5/190°C/375°F.
Grease a 2 pint (1 litre) ovenproof dish.

• Put the lentils in a pan with the stock cube and the savory. Cover with water, bring to the boil then simmer, covered, on a low heat for 20 minutes until the lentils are soft and mushy. (Add more water as necessary and stir regularly to prevent sticking).
• Fry the onion, garlic and mushrooms in the margarine until softening.
• Mix the fried vegetables with the lentils, cashew nuts, mashed potato, parsley, nutmeg and pepper.
• Pile into the prepared dish and fork up the top to make it look attractive. Bake for 25–30 minutes until the potato is brown and crispy.
• Serve with steamed green vegetables.
• Freeze unbaked, thaw and bake.
*Note:* I normally leave the skins on the potatoes, even for mashing. This is not only better nutritionally but gives a better flavour and texture.


**Bean and Vegetable Crumble**

This tasty mixture of beans and seasonal vegetables with a crunchy crumble topping amazes people who think that crumbles have to be sweet. A good recipe for using up odd vegetables left over from another dish.

*Base:*
1½ lb (675 g) diced vegetables (e.g. onion, mushrooms, courgettes, carrots, cauliflower, peppers, swede, celery, etc.)
4 oz (100 g) beans — any variety
Medium tin tomatoes, chopped
1 tablespoon oil
1 vegetable stock cube
1 tablespoon tomato purée
1 clove garlic, crushed
2 teaspoons basil
Black pepper

*Crumble:*
6 oz (175 g) wholemeal flour
3 oz (75 g) margarine
1 tablespoon sunflower or pumpkin seeds
1 tablespoon rolled oats
1 tablespoon ground hazelnuts
1 tablespoon toasted wheatflakes (optional)

### Method

Set oven to Gas 5/190°C/375°F.
Grease a 2 pint (1 litre) ovenproof dish.

- Presoak and cook the beans. Drain and reserve liquid.
- Fry the vegetables and garlic in the oil for a few minutes until softening.
- Make the bean water up to ½ pint (275 ml) and add to the vegetables with the stock cube, tomatoes, tomato puree, basil and pepper.
- Bring to the boil, cover and simmer on a low heat for 15–20 minutes until the vegetables are cooked and the liquid thickened. Add the cooked beans and stir well.
- Pour into the prepared dish.
- Rub the margarine into the flour until the mixture resembles fine breadcrumbs. Add the oats, nuts, seeds and wheatflakes. Stir well.
- Sprinkle the crumble on top of the vegetables. Bake for 20 minutes until golden and crispy.
- Serve with potatoes and green salad.
- Freeze unbaked and bake on thawing.

*Variation:* The vegetable mixture can be curried for a change, using 3–4 teaspoons curry powder in place of the basil.

### Green Lentil and Fennel Crumble

The delicate flavour of fennel goes particularly well with lentils and as green lentils hold their shape so well when cooked they are ideal in this dish.

*Base:*
8 oz (225 g) green lentils, washed thoroughly
1 lb (450 g) fennel, chopped (white parts and leaves)
1 onion, chopped

164

2 cloves garlic, crushed
2 courgettes, chopped
1 tablespoon oil
1 medium tin tomatoes chopped
1 pint (500 ml) stock
2 tablespoons tomato purée
2 teaspoons marjoram
2 bayleaves
2 tablespoons fresh chopped parsley
Pepper

*Crumble:*
6 oz (175 g) flour
3 oz (75 g) margarine
1 tablespoon sunflower seeds
1 tablespoon rolled oats
1 tablespoon ground nuts
1 tablespoon toasted wheatflakes (optional)

### Method

Set oven to Gas 5/190°C/375°F.
Grease a 2 pint (1 litre) ovenproof dish.

• Fry the fennel, onion, garlic and courgettes in the oil until softening.
• Add the lentils, tomatoes, stock, tomato purée, marjoram, bayleaves and pepper. Bring to the boil, cover and simmer on a low heat for 30 minutes until the lentils are cooked and most of the liquid is absorbed. Stir regularly to prevent sticking.
• Stir in the parsley and pour into the prepared dish.
• Rub the margarine into the flour until the mixture resembles breadcrumbs. Stir in the oats, nuts, seeds and wheatflakes.
• Sprinkle the crumble mixture on top of the lentil mixture. Bake for 20 minutes until brown and crispy.
• Serve with potatoes and green salad.
• Freeze unbaked and bake on thawing.


**Spicy Chick-Pea Cobbler**

This tasty dish is very filling and ideal for hungry families as a

165

change from a pie. Serve with a crisp salad.

*Base*:
4 oz (100 g) chick peas
1 onion, chopped
1 clove garlic, crushed
Knob fresh ginger, peeled and grated
1 stick celery, chopped
1 large carrot, chopped
2 oz (50 g) mushrooms, sliced
2 oz (50 g) fresh or frozen peas
4 oz (100 g) cauliflower florets, broken into small pieces
1 tablespoon oil
1 stock cube or 1 teaspoon stock concentrate
2 teaspoons pickle
1 tablespoon tomato purée
1 teaspoon wholegrain mustard
2 teaspoons curry powder
Black pepper

*Cobbler*:
4 oz (100 g) wholemeal flour
2 teaspoons baking powder
1 oz (25 g) margarine
1 tablespoon fresh chopped parsley
2–3 fl oz (50–75 ml) soya milk

**Method**

Set oven to Gas 8/230°C/450°F.
Grease a 2 pint (1 litre) ovenproof dish.

• Presoak and cook the chick peas. Drain and reserve liquid.
• Fry the onion, garlic, ginger, celery, carrot, mushrooms, peas and cauliflower in the oil until just softening.
• Make the chick pea cooking water up to $\frac{1}{2}$ pint (275 ml) and add to the vegetables with the stock cube, pickle, tomato purée, mustard, curry powder and pepper. Bring to the boil, cover and simmer for 10 minutes stirring occasionally until the vegetables are cooked and the liquid has reduced and thickened.
• *Meanwhile make the cobbler topping* — rub the margarine into the flour and baking powder until the mixture resembles breadcrumbs.

- Add the parsley and enough soya milk from the 2–3 fl oz (50–75 ml) to form a moist, firm dough. Knead lightly until smooth.
- Add the cooked chick peas to the vegetable mixture and pour into the prepared dish.
- Roll the scone mixture out on a well floured board until it is about $\frac{1}{2}''$ (1 cm) thick and will fit the top of the chick pea mixture. Lay on top of the vegetables.
- Score the top of the scone with a sharp knife in a criss-cross pattern and brush with remaining soya milk.
- Bake for 10–15 minutes until the scone is risen and brown. Serve immediately.
- Freezes well raw or cooked, but eat within 6 weeks because the spices intensify in flavour after this time.

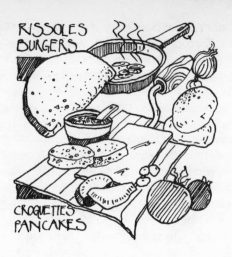

## Nutty Parsnip Rissoles

These delicious, crispy balls have a lovely sweet flavour and are high in protein. They look very attractive served in sweet and sour or barbecue sauce like vegan meatballs! (Makes 12.)

        8 oz (225 g) wholemeal breadcrumbs
        8 oz (225 g) ground nuts (e.g. hazels, almonds, walnuts)
        1 large onion, finely chopped
        1 clove garlic, crushed
        8 oz (225 g) cooking apples, peeled, cored and grated
        8 oz (225 g) parsnip scrubbed and grated
        Knob margarine
        1 tablespoon tomato purée
        1 teaspoon yeast extract or miso
        Rind and juice 1 small lemon
        1 tablespoon fresh chopped parsley
        1 teaspoon sage
        1 teaspoon ground coriander
        2 tablespoons stock
        Pepper
        Flour to coat
        Oil to fry

### Method

- Melt margarine and fry onion, garlic, apple and parsnip for 2–3 minutes until softening.
- Add the breadcrumbs, nuts, tomato purée, yeast extract/

miso, lemon rind and juice, parsley, sage, coriander and pepper. Mix thoroughly.
• Add the stock and knead well to a stiffish mixture. (More stock may be added if the mixture is too dry but do not make it too wet).
• Divide the mixture into 12 balls and coat each one with flour. Fry in hot oil for 2–3 minutes until brown and crispy.
• Serve separately with a jug of sauce or heat through in sauce in the oven. Delicious with jacket potatoes and green salad. Mixture can be used to make small balls to serve on cocktail sticks for buffet parties.
• Better frozen raw and fried from frozen.


## Tofu Burgers

Tasty and extremely nutritious, these burgers have no cholesterol and are lower in calories than most. Very popular with children especially if served in wholemeal baps with relishes and salad. (Makes 8.)

> 8 oz (225 g) *firm* tofu, drained and mashed
> 8 oz (225 g) wholemeal breadcrumbs
> Knob margarine
> 1 onion, finely chopped
> 4 oz (100 g) mushrooms, finely chopped
> 2 carrots, grated
> 2 cloves garlic, crushed
> 1 dessertspoon tomato purée
> 1 tablespoon soy sauce
> 1 teaspoon dried mace
> 1 teaspoon thyme
> 1 teaspoon yeast extract/miso
> Pepper to taste
> Wholemeal flour to coat
> Oil to fry

### Method

• Fry the onion, garlic, carrot and mushrooms in the margarine until soft.
• Add the mashed tofu, breadcrumbs, tomato purée, soy sauce, mace, thyme, yeast extract/miso and pepper. Mix thoroughly with the hands.

- Divide the mixture into 8 balls and shape each into a burger. Coat in flour.
- Fry in hot oil for 2–3 minutes until brown and crispy.
- Serve with tomato, barbecue or sweet and sour sauce, jacket potatoes and salad.
- Better frozen raw and fried from frozen.


## Millet Burgers

Deliciously crispy on the outside but soft on the inside, these filling burgers have a unique taste and texture. (Makes 12). *This recipe is dedicated to Sue.*

> 8 oz (225 g) millet seed
> 1 stock cube
> Pinch mixed herbs
> 2 bay leaves
> 1 teaspoon yeast extract
> 2–4 oz (50–100 g) wholemeal breadcrumbs
> 1 tablespoon oil
> 1 large onion, chopped finely
> 2 cloves garlic, crushed
> ½ pepper, finely chopped
> 1 stick celery, finely chopped
> 2 carrots, grated
> 2 oz (50 g) mushrooms, chopped
> 1 teaspoon nutmeg
> 1 teaspoon coriander
> 1 tablespoon soy sauce
> 1 tablespoon fresh chopped parsley
> Pepper
> Flour to coat
> Oil to fry

### Method

- Put the millet in a pan with the stock cube, herbs, bay leaves and yeast extract. Cover with water, bring to the boil and simmer, covered, until millet is swollen and mushy. Add more water during cooking as necessary and stir regularly to prevent sticking.
- Fry the onion, garlic, pepper, mushrooms, celery and carrots in the oil until soft.

- Add the cooked millet, nutmeg, coriander, soy sauce, parsley and pepper. Mix thoroughly.
- Add enough breadcrumbs to make a stiff mixture capable of being shaped and knead in well.
- Shape into 12 round burgers, coat in flour and fry in hot oil for 2–3 minutes until brown and crisp.
- Serve with peanut or barbecue sauce and salad.
- Better frozen raw and fried from frozen.
- As these burgers are made entirely from grain it is advisable to serve them with a pulse dish e.g. bean salad or tofu dessert to achieve good protein complementarity.

## Bean Croquettes

These vegan 'sausages' are a firm favourite and are absolutely delicious hot or cold. (Makes 8).

> 6 oz (175 g) white beans (e.g. haricot, butter, black-eye)
> 6–8 oz (175–225 g) wholemeal breadcrumbs
> Knob margarine
> 1 large onion, finely chopped
> 2 cloves garlic, crushed
> Rind and juice 1 small lemon
> 1 tablespoon tomato purée
> 1 teaspoon yeast extract/miso
> 1 teaspoon sage
> 1 teaspoon thyme
> 1 tablespoon fresh chopped parsley
> 1 teaspoon nutmeg
> Pepper
> Flour to coat
> Oil to fry

### Method

- Presoak and cook the beans. Drain and reserve liquid.
- Melt margarine and fry the onion and garlic until soft.
- Add the lemon rind and juice, tomato purée, yeast extract/miso, thyme, sage, parsley, nutmeg and pepper.
- Mash or liquidize the beans to a smooth purée using some of the cooking water to moisten. Try not to make it too wet. Add to the ingredients in the pan and mix thoroughly.
- Add enough breadcrumbs to make a stiff mixture capable

of being shaped without being sticky. (The amount required will depend on how wet the bean mixture is).

- Shape into 8 croquettes or 'sausages' and roll in flour.
- Fry in hot oil for 2–3 minutes turning frequently until brown and crispy.
- Serve with mustard, garlic and tarragon sauce and salad.
- Better frozen raw and then fried from frozen.
- The mixture can be used to make small 'sausages' (ideal for buffets) on sticks or as a 'sausage' roll filling with wholemeal flaky pastry.


## Lentil Burgers

These tasty burgers are extremely nutritious and have a lovely moist texture. Another popular one with children when served in a bap with relishes. (Makes 8).

8 oz (225 g) red lentils, washed thoroughly
8 oz (225 g) wholemeal breadcrumbs
1 stock cube or teaspoon stock concentrate
1 teaspoon thyme
2 cloves garlic, crushed
1 large onion, chopped
1 tablespoon oil
1 tablespoon tomato purée
1 teaspoon nutmeg
1 teaspoon cumin
1 teaspoon yeast extract
1 tablespoon fresh parsley, chopped
Pepper
Wholemeal flour to coat
Oil to fry

### Method

- Put the lentils, stock cube and thyme in a pan with enough water to cover. Cook until soft and mushy. (Add more water during cooking if necessary but do not make the purée too wet).
- Fry the onion and garlic in the oil for a few minutes until softening.
- Mix the lentils, onion, garlic, breadcrumbs, tomato purée, nutmeg, cumin, yeast extract and parsley together. Season with pepper.

- Divide into 8 balls and shape each into a flat burger. Coat in flour and fry in hot oil for 2–3 minutes until brown and crisp.
- Serve with onion, sweet and sour or mushroom sauce, jacket potatoes and salad.
- Better frozen raw and fried from frozen.


## Herby Yellow Split Pea Croquettes

These tasty croquettes are very popular with children and are equally nice hot or cold. The mixture can be used to make small 'sausages' for cocktail parties. (Makes 8.)

8 oz (225 g) yellow split peas, washed thoroughly
1 stock cube
2 bay leaves
1 teaspoon savory
2 teaspoons tarragon
1 onion, chopped finely
2 cloves garlic, crushed
Knob margarine
2 tablespoons fresh chopped parsley
Rind 1 small lemon
1 tablespoon soy sauce
6 oz (175 g) wholemeal breadcrumbs
Pepper
Flour to coat
Oil to fry

### Method

- Put the split peas, stock cube, bay leaves, savory and tarragon in a pan, cover with water and bring to the boil. Cover and simmer on a low heat for 40 minutes until the peas are soft and mushy. (Add more water during cooking if necessary and stir regularly to prevent sticking). Remove bay leaves.
- Fry the onion and garlic in the margarine until softening. Add to the split pea purée with the parsley, lemon rind, soy sauce, breadcrumbs and pepper.
- Mix thoroughly and shape into 8 croquettes. Coat each one in flour and fry in hot oil for 2–3 minutes until crisp and brown.
- Serve with mushroom or mustard sauce, new potatoes and salad.
- Freeze uncooked and fry from frozen.

## Vegetable Burgers

These light crispy burgers are ideal for summer meals or buffets as they can be served hot or cold. Protein is provided by the beansprouts, soya milk sauce and breadcrumbs so they are very nutritious. The vegetables must be finely chopped or the burgers are very difficult to shape. (Makes 8).

1 oz (25 g) margarine
1 onion, *finely* chopped
4 oz (100 g) mushrooms, *finely* chopped
1 clove garlic, crushed
2 carrots, grated
1 stick celery, *finely* chopped
½ green pepper, *finely* chopped
1 courgette, *finely* chopped
4 oz (100 g) lentil or mungbean sprouts, chopped
1 oz (25 g) flour
¼ pint (150 ml) soya milk
½ stock cube
2 tablespoons fresh chopped parsley
1 teaspoon tarragon
1 teaspoon miso
8 oz (225 g) breadcrumbs
Pepper
Flour to coat
Oil to fry

*Method*

• Fry the onion, mushrooms, garlic, carrots, celery, pepper and courgette in the margarine until soft. Cover and leave to 'sweat' for 5 minutes.
• Add the beansprouts and flour and cook for one minute.
• *Remove from heat* and stir in the soya milk gradually to form a thick mixture. Add the stock cube, parsley, tarragon and pepper.
• Return to low heat and stir until the sauce is thick and the stock cube has dissolved. Remove from heat again and stir in the miso.
• Add the breadcrumbs and mix thoroughly to form a stiff paste capable of being shaped into burgers. Allow to cool slightly.
• Divide the mixture into 8 balls and shape each into a flat

burger. Coat in flour and fry in hot oil for 2–3 minutes until brown and crisp.
• Serve with tomato, ginger and mushroom; barbecue, sweet and sour or curry sauce and salad.
• Freeze raw and fry from frozen.


## Adzuki and Brazil Nut Burgers

These tasty burgers are delicious hot or cold and are very popular in baps with relishes and salad. (Makes 8.)

> 6 oz (175 g) adzuki beans
> 6 oz (175 g) ground brazil nuts
> 3 oz (75 g) breadcrumbs
> 1 onion, finely chopped
> 2 cloves garlic, crushed
> ½ green pepper, chopped
> Knob margarine
> 2 tablespoons fresh chopped parsley
> 2 teaspoons sage
> 2 teaspoons wholegrain mustard
> 2 teaspoons coriander
> 1 teaspoon yeast extract
> Pepper
> Flour to coat
> Oil to fry


*Method*

• Presoak and cook the adzuki beans. Drain and reserve liquid.
• Fry the onion, garlic and pepper in the margarine until softening.
• Liquidize or mash the cooked beans to a stiff paste with 2 or 3 tablespoons of reserved liquid.
• Add the cooked vegetables, brazil nuts, parsley, sage, mustard, coriander, yeast extract and pepper. Mix to a stiff paste and add enough breadcrumbs to make the mixture firm enough to shape (3 oz/75 g is usually enough depending on how wet the adzuki bean puree was).
• Divide the mixture into 8 balls and shape each into a burger. Coat in flour.

175

- Fry in hot oil for 2–3 minutes until brown and crispy. Serve with onion; tahini and miso or parsley and tarragon sauce, potatoes and salad.
- Freeze raw, pack in bags and fry from frozen.

## Felafels

These spicy Middle Eastern chick pea balls are delicious hot or cold. Traditionally they do not contain breadcrumbs but I find this helps them to bind together better and also improves their protein content. (Makes 8.)

> 8 oz (225 g) chick peas
> 4 oz (100 g) wholemeal breadcrumbs
> 1 large onion, very finely chopped
> 2 cloves garlic; crushed
> Knob fresh ginger, peeled and grated
> 1 tablespoon tomato purée
> Knob margarine
> 2 teaspoons coriander
> 2 teaspoons cumin
> 2 teaspoons garam masala
> 1 teaspoon ground cardamom
> 1 dessertspoon soy sauce
> Pepper
> Flour to coat
> Oil to fry

### Method

- Presoak the chick peas and cook. Drain and reserve liquid.
- Fry the onion, garlic and ginger in the margarine until softening and put in a bowl with the breadcrumbs, soy sauce, spices, tomato puree and pepper.
- Mash or liquidize the chick peas with 2–3 tablespoons of the reserved liquid to form a stiff paste.
- Add the chick pea puree to the ingredients in the bowl and mix thoroughly. Divide into 8 balls and coat each one in wholemeal flour.
- Fry in hot oil for 2–3 minutes until golden and crispy. Serve with curry sauce or tomato sauce and a green salad.
- Freeze raw and fry from frozen.

*Note:* If the mixture is very soft, add some more breadcrumbs or chill for 30 minutes prior to frying.

## Chick-pea Samosas

These delicious deep-fried curry parcels are ideal for picnics and lunch boxes served cold, or they may be served hot as a main course. They are a lot easier to make than they seem!

*Pastry:*
4 oz (100 g) wholemeal flour
½ oz (12 g) melted margarine
3–4 fl oz (75–100 ml) cold water

*Filling:*
2 oz (50 g) chick peas (*or 4 oz (100 g) tinned ones*)
1 small onion, very finely chopped
1 clove garlic, crushed
2 small carrots, very finely diced
1 medium potato, very finely diced
4 oz (100 g) cauliflower florets broken into small pieces
2 oz (50 g) fresh or frozen peas
½ stock cube or ½ teaspoon stock concentrate
1 tablespoon oil
½ teaspoon cayenne pepper
1 teaspoon curry powder
1 teaspoon wholegrain mustard
2 teaspoons pickle
1 teaspoon turmeric
1 teaspoon cumin
1 teaspoon coriander
1 teaspoon garam masala
Oil for deep frying

## *Method*

*Make filling first:* Presoak and cook the chick peas. Drain and reserve liquid.
• Fry the onion, garlic, carrot, potato, cauliflower and peas in the oil until softening.
• Add the cayenne pepper, curry powder, mustard, pickle, turmeric, cumin, coriander and fry for a further 2 minutes, stirring continuously.

177

- Add the stock cube or stock concentrate and ¼ pint (150 ml) reserved chick-pea liquid. Bring to the boil then lower heat, cover and simmer for 10–15 minutes until the vegetables are soft and all the liquid is absorbed.
- Add the cooked chickpeas and garam masala. Stir well then allow to *cool* while you make the pastry.
- *To make pastry* — mix the flour and melted margarine, then add enough cold water to make a smooth, non-sticky dough that leaves the sides of the bowl clean. (3 or 4 fl oz (75–100 ml) water will be enough).
- Knead the dough well until it is smooth and elastic and divide into 6 small balls the size of a walnut.
- Roll each ball out on a floured board to a thin saucer-sized circle. (Try to make the pastry as thin as possible).
- Cut each circle in half to form 12 semi-circles. Place a dessertspoonful of *cold* filling on each semi-circle of pastry. (*It is important to let the filling cool or it will make the pastry soggy*). See Fig. 4.
- Brush the edges with water, then fold the pastry over the filling and seal the edges well by pinching together to form 12 triangular parcels.
- Heat some oil in a wok or deep saucepan until almost smoking. Deep fry the samosas, a few at a time, for about 5 minutes until they are puffed out and crispy brown.
- Drain on absorbent paper and serve immediately, allowing 3 per person for a main course. Alternatively, allow to cool and serve as a picnic item.
- Store in an airtight container in the fridge. They will keep 3 days and may be crisped up again by reheating for 15 minutes in a low oven Gas 4/180°C/350°F.
- Better frozen raw before frying and then deep fried from frozen.

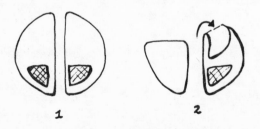

**Figure 4**

178

## Savoury Stuffed Pancakes

Stuffed pancakes make a very impressive dinner party main course but are equally versatile for everyday family meals. The basic recipe with some variations is given below and suggested tasty fillings follow.

*Basic pancake recipe* (makes 8)

> 4 oz (100 g) wholemeal flour
> 1 rounded tablespoon soya flour
> 1 rounded tablespoon chick pea (Gram) flour
> 12 fl oz (325 ml) soya milk
> 1 tablespoon oil
> 1 teaspoon baking powder
> Oil to fry
> Filling of your choice

*Method*

• Whizz all the ingredients (except the frying oil) together in a liquidizer or whisk with a balloon whisk until smooth. Allow to stand for 30 minutes.
• Whisk the batter again before frying. Pour into a jug.
• Heat a drop of oil in a frying pan or omelette pan until nearly smoking. Pour about 3 tablespoons of batter into the pan and tilt so the batter runs all over the base of the pan. Lower the heat slightly.
• Fry for about one minute or until brown on the underside. Ease with a palette knife or fish slice and flip over. Fry the other side until brown then slide the pancake onto a tray covered in greaseproof or kitchen paper.
• Fry the other 7 pancakes in the same way adding a drop of oil to the pan in between each one and checking that the pan is not too hot. (The batter should sizzle as it hits the pan but the fat should not be smoking or it has overheated).
• Put a tablespoonful of your (warm) chosen filling on the edge of each pancake and roll it up to encase the filling.
• Lay the pancake rolls on a lightly greased tray, cover with foil and reheat for 20 minutes Gas 4/180°C/350°F. (Alternatively serve straight from the pan one at a time, filling and rolling as you go — this is alright if the family don't mind waiting but if you all want to eat together the reheating method is easier).

179

- Serve the pancakes plain or with a complementing sauce over the top to add a luxurious touch (see suggestions with filling recipes). Serve with salad or green vegetables.

*Note:* The batter is rich in protein so it is not *essential* to include nuts, pulses or grains in the filling.

- *Freezing:* The pancakes can be frozen unfilled in layers with greaseproof paper in between each one or may be frozen filled, on trays and then packed into bags. The fillings will freeze in plastic containers and can be thawed and used as required.

- Variations

*Parsley pancakes:* add 2 tablespoons chopped fresh parsley to the batter.

*Nutty pancakes:* add 1 oz (25 g) ground nuts (hazels, cashews or almonds) to the batter and 2–3 tablespoons water to thin it down.

*Spicy pancakes:* add 1–2 teaspoons of your favourite spice to the batter — try cumin, coriander or nutmeg.

*Buckwheat pancakes:* Substitute 2 oz (50 g) of the flour for buckwheat flour to produce a speckled pancake with a characteristic savoury flavour.


**Fennel Ratatouille**

This tasty mixture is quick to make and very popular. The fennel gives an interesting variation in flavour.

(To fill 8 pancakes)
    1 small or ½ large aubergine, chopped
    2 courgettes, chopped
    1 small onion, chopped
    4 oz (100 g) mushrooms, sliced
    ½ red or green pepper, sliced
    1 head fennel, sliced
    1 clove garlic, crushed
    1 small tin tomatoes, chopped or liquidized
    1 tablespoon tomato purée
    1 teaspoon basil
    1 tablespoon olive oil
    Pepper

*Method*

• Fry the aubergine, courgettes, onion, mushrooms, pepper, fennel and garlic in the oil until softening.
• Cover and allow to 'sweat' for 5 minutes.
• Add the tomatoes, tomato purée, basil and pepper. Bring to the boil, cover and simmer on a low heat for 10 minutes until the vegetables are soft.
• Use to fill pancakes while still warm.
• This filling goes particularly well with parsley and tarragon or miso and tahini sauce.


## Chinese Vegetable

An authentic tasting mixture of stir-fried vegetables makes a very unusual filling for pancakes. Very quick to make.

(To fill 8 pancakes)

> 4 oz (100 g) cauliflower florets broken into *small* pieces.
> 4 oz (100 g) tinned bamboo shoots, sliced *thinly*
> 8 oz (225 g) mung bean sprouts
> Knob fresh ginger, peeled and grated
> 2 cloves garlic, crushed
> 1 onion, *thinly* sliced
> 1 green pepper, *thinly* sliced
> 4 oz (100 g) mushrooms, *thinly* sliced
> 2 tablespoons sesame, soya or olive oil
> 3 tablespoons soy sauce
> 2 teaspoons coriander
> Pepper


*Method*

• Heat the oil in a wok or large pan and tip in the cauliflower, bamboo shoots, ginger, garlic, onion, pepper and mushrooms. Toss in the oil for 3 minutes.
• Add the beansprouts and toss for 1 minute.
• Add the soy sauce, pepper and coriander. Stir in, cover and 'sweat' for 2 minutes.
• Use to fill pancakes immediately whilst still crisp.
• This filling goes particularly well with sweet and sour sauce.

## Pinto Bean, Spinach and Mushroom

A lovely combination of flavours and textures. Any beans may be used in place of the pinto beans if they are not available.

(To fill 8 pancakes)

4 oz (100 g) pinto beans
1 lb (500 g) frozen or fresh spinach, chopped
2 onions, chopped
8 oz (225 g) mushrooms, sliced
2 cloves garlic, crushed
Knob margarine
2 teaspoons nutmeg
2 tablespoons tomato purée
Pepper

### *Method*

• Presoak and cook the beans. Drain and reserve liquid.
• Melt the margarine and add the onions, garlic, mushrooms and spinach. (If using frozen spinach, do not thaw, but fry from frozen). Fry for 5 minutes until soft and the spinach (if frozen) is thawed.
• Add the cooked beans, nutmeg, tomato purée and pepper. Fry for a further minute to heat through thoroughly.
• Use to fill pancakes whilst still warm.
• This filling goes particularly well with mustard or tahini and miso sauce.

## Vegetable Rice

A quick and easy filling that is useful for using up odd vegetables.

(To fill 8 pancakes)

2 oz (50 g) long-grain brown rice, washed
1 tablespoon oil
1 small onion, chopped
½ green or red pepper, chopped
2 courgettes, sliced

1 tablespoon frozen or tinned sweetcorn
2 oz (50 g) cauliflower florets, broken into small pieces
2 oz (50 g) fresh or frozen peas
1 clove garlic
1 small tin tomatoes, chopped
1 tablespoon fresh chopped parsley
1 teaspoon basil
1 tablespoon tomato purée
Pepper

*Method*

• Cook the rice until soft. Drain and rinse to separate the grains.
• Fry the onion, pepper, courgettes, corn, cauliflower, peas and garlic in the oil until softening.
• Add the tomatoes, parsley, basil, tomato purée and pepper. Bring to the boil, cover and simmer on a low heat for 10 minutes until the vegetables are cooked and the liquid thickened.
• Stir in the cooked rice and use to fill pancakes whilst still warm.
• This filling goes well with mushroom; parsley and tarragon or lemon and coriander sauce.

## Green Lentil and Mushroom

A lovely rich filling that is easy to make. Use mature 'flat' mushrooms for a superior flavour.

(To fill 8 pancakes)

4 oz (100 g) green lentils, washed thoroughly
1 stock cube
1 teaspoon savory
1 bay leaf
Knob margarine
6 oz (175 g) flat mushrooms, sliced
1 small onion, chopped
2 cloves garlic, crushed
2 teaspoons wholegrain mustard
1 dessertspoon soy sauce
Pepper

183

## Method

- Put the lentils in a pan with the stock cube, savory and bayleaf. Cover with water and bring to the boil. Skim off any froth then reduce the heat and simmer for 30 minutes until the lentils are soft and can be mashed roughly. (Add more water as necessary during cooking but do not make the mixture too wet).
- Fry the mushrooms, onion and garlic in the margarine until softening then mix in the cooked lentils, mustard, soy sauce and pepper. Remove bayleaf.
- Use to fill pancakes whilst still warm.
- This filling goes particularly well with tomato, sweet and sour or barbecue sauce.


## Vegetable Curry

A mild vegetable curry makes a tasty and unusual pancake filling. Useful for using up odd vegetables.

(To fill 8 pancakes)

> $1\frac{1}{4}$ lb (550 g) mixed seasonal vegetables, diced (e.g. potato, carrot, swede, cauliflower, courgettes, peppers, aubergine, celery etc.)
> 1 large onion, chopped
> 1 clove garlic, crushed
> Knob fresh ginger, peeled and grated
> 1 tablespoon oil
> 2 teaspoons curry powder
> 1 teaspoon cumin
> 1 teaspoon coriander
> 1 teaspoon pickle
> $\frac{1}{2}$ pint (275 ml) stock
> 1 tablespoon tomato purée
> Pepper


## Method

- Fry the vegetables, onion, garlic and ginger in the oil for a few minutes until softening. Cover and 'sweat' for 5 minutes.
- Add the curry powder, cumin, coriander and pickle and fry for 1 minute.

- Add the stock, tomato purée and pepper. Cover and simmer for 30–40 minutes until the vegetables are cooked and all the liquid has been absorbed.
- Use to fill pancakes whilst still warm.
- This filling goes well with lemon and coriander or tahini and miso sauce

## Lentil Lasagne

Quick to prepare, tasty and highly nutritious, this dish is unfailingly popular. *This recipe is dedicated to Fiona.*

*Base*
>    8 oz (225 g) wholewheat or spinach lasagne (about 12 sheets)
>    6 oz (175 g) red lentils, washed thoroughly
>    1 onion, chopped
>    2 cloves garlic, crushed
>    2 tablespoons sweetcorn (tinned or frozen)
>    1 red pepper, sliced
>    4 oz (100 g) mushrooms, sliced
>    1 head fennel, chopped
>    2 sticks celery, chopped
>    1 tablespoon olive oil
>    Medium tin tomatoes, liquidized or chopped
>    ½ pint (275 ml) stock
>    1 tablespoon tomato purée
>    2 teaspoons oregano
>    2 teaspoons basil
>    1 tablespoon fresh chopped parsley
>    Pepper

*Topping*
>    4 oz (100 g) wholewheat breadcrumbs
>    2 oz (50 g) sunflower seeds
>    2 oz (50 g) margarine
>    1 tablespoon fresh chopped parsley

## Method

Set oven to Gas 5/190°F/375°F.
Grease a 3 pint (1½ litre) ovenproof dish or baking tin.

• *First make the sauce:* fry all the vegetables and garlic in the olive oil until softening.
• Add the washed lentils, tomatoes, stock, tomato purée, herbs, parsley and pepper. Bring to the boil, reduce heat, cover and simmer for 15 minutes until the lentils are soft and swollen and most of the liquid has been absorbed. Remove from heat.
• Cook the lasagne in boiling water with a drop of oil added for 12 minutes, or according to instructions on packet. Stir occasionally to prevent sheets sticking together. Drain.
• Put one third of the lasagne on the base of the dish and pour a third of the lentil sauce over.
• Add another layer of lasagne, then lentils, then lasagne and a final layer of lentils.
• *To make topping:* Melt the margarine and stir in the breadcrumbs, sunflower seeds and parsley until well coated. Sprinkle on top of the lasagne.
• Bake for 20 minutes until the top is brown and crispy. Serve with salad or green vegetables.
• Freezes well uncooked or cooked.


## Tofu Lasagne

This is a tasty, vegan version of a very popular dish. The combination of wheat pasta and tofu makes the lasagne very high in protein but it is low in fat. The lasagne sauce may also be served with other pastas such as spaghetti for a quick meal. (Serves 4–6.)

8 oz (225 g) wholewheat or spinach lasagne (about 12 sheets)
12 oz (350 g) *silken* tofu
6 tablespoons water
2 teaspoons soy sauce
1 teaspoon mixed herbs
1 teaspoon cayenne pepper
1 teaspoon wholegrain mustard
1 clove garlic, crushed
Black pepper

187

2 tablespoons sesame seeds

*For the sauce*
   1 tablespoon olive oil
   1 onion, chopped
   2 cloves garlic, crushed
   2 small courgettes, diced
   1 small aubergine, diced
   1 red pepper, chopped
   4 oz (100 g) mushrooms, sliced
   Small head of fennel, chopped
   Medium tin tomatoes, liquidized or chopped
   1 tablespoon tomato purée
   2 teaspoons basil
   Black pepper

### Method

Set oven to Gas 5/190°C/375°F.
Grease a 3 pint (1½ litre) ovenproof dish or baking tin.

- *First make the sauce* — fry all the vegetables and garlic in the oil until softening. Reduce heat, cover and allow to 'sweat' for 5 minutes.
- Add the tinned tomatoes, tomato purée, basil and pepper. Simmer, covered, for 10 minutes until the vegetables are soft and the liquid thickened. Remove from heat.
- Cook the lasagne in boiling water with a drop of oil added for 12 minutes, or according to instructions on packet. Stir occasionally to prevent sheets sticking together. Drain.
- Put the tofu, water, soy sauce, herbs, cayenne pepper, mustard, garlic and pepper in a liquidizer and whizz to form a smooth cream.
- Put one third of the lasagne on the base of the prepared dish and spread half the tomato sauce on top. Pour a third of the tofu mixture over this.
- Cover with another layer of lasagne and the rest of the tomato sauce. Finish with a final layer of lasagne.
- Pour the remaining two-thirds of the tofu mixture over the lasagne and smooth over. Sprinkle with sesame seeds.
- Bake for 30 minutes until the tofu is set and well browned. Serve immediately with a green salad or green vegetables.
- When frozen the tofu goes a bit chewy.

## Tofu, Peanut and Macaroni Savoury

This dish is packed with nutrients and works equally well with noodles, spaghetti, tagliatelle or pasta shells in place of macaroni. A quick and easy meal to prepare.

12 oz (350 g) wholewheat macaroni
1 large onion, chopped
2 cloves garlic, crushed
1 pepper, sliced
4 oz (100 g) mushrooms, sliced
Knob margarine
Medium tin tomatoes chopped/liquidized
1 tablespoon tomato purée
1 tablespoon soy sauce
½ pint (275 ml) stock
1 teaspoon basil
1 teaspoon coriander
8 oz (225 g) *firm* tofu cut into small cubes
4 oz (100 g) salted peanuts
Black pepper

### *Method*

• Cook the macaroni in boiling water with a drop of oil added for 10 minutes or according to instructions on packet. Drain.
• Fry onion, garlic, pepper and mushrooms in the margarine for a few minutes until soft. Add tinned tomatoes, stock, tomato purée, soy sauce, basil, coriander and tofu cubes. Season well.
• Bring to the boil then simmer for 10 minutes stirring occasionally.
• Add the peanuts and cooked macaroni and heat through for 5 minutes, stirring continuously.
• Serve immediately with a green salad.
• Can be frozen but tofu will go slightly chewy.

## Pasta and Vegetable Savoury

Any pasta can be used in this quick, tasty dish which is suitable for a family meal.

8 oz (225 g) pasta (e.g. shells, twists, macaroni etc.)
1 onion, sliced
½ red pepper, sliced
4 courgettes, chopped
2 cloves garlic, crushed
4 oz (100 g) mushrooms, sliced
2 sticks celery, chopped
1 small tin sweetcorn, drained
4 oz (100 g) beansprouts (any variety)
2 oz (50 g) margarine
2 oz (50 g) flour
1 pint (500 ml) soya milk
2 teaspoons miso
2 tablespoons fresh chopped parsley
1 tablespoon soy sauce
2 teaspoons coriander
Pepper

## Method

- Cook the pasta in boiling water with a drop of oil added for 10 minutes or according to instructions on packet. Drain.
- Fry the onion, pepper, courgettes, garlic, mushrooms, celery and corn in the margarine until softening.
- Stir in the flour and cook for a further minute.
- *Remove from heat* and stir in the soya milk gradually, until a smooth sauce is formed. Add the parsley, soy sauce, coriander and pepper.
- Return to a low heat and cook, stirring, until the sauce is bubbling and has thickened.
- Add the cooked pasta, beansprouts and miso, stir and bring gently to serving temperature. *Do not boil or the beneficial enzymes in the miso will be destroyed.*
- Serve immediately with a green salad.
- Can be frozen but may need more soya milk adding after thawing before reheating *gently* in a pan.

## Spicy Bean Pasta

A tasty and unusual dish which can be adapted for use with any pasta or beans. It is very easy to make despite the long list of ingredients.

4 oz (100 g) beans (e.g. pinto, kidney, haricot)
8 oz (225 g) pasta (e.g. twists, shells, tagliatelle)
3 carrots, chopped
1 onion, chopped
2 cloves garlic, crushed
Knob fresh ginger, peeled and grated
4 courgettes, chopped
1 pepper, chopped
4 oz (100 g) cauliflower florets broken into small pieces
4 oz (100 g) mushrooms, sliced
4 oz (100 g) fresh or frozen peas
1 tablespoon oil
1 stock cube
2 tablespoons tomato purée
2 teaspoons pickle
1 teaspoon wholegrain mustard
$\frac{1}{4}$ teaspoon tabasco sauce (optional)
$\frac{1}{2}$ teaspoon mace
2 teaspoons cumin
2 teaspoons coriander
2 teaspoons turmeric
1 teaspoon ground cardamom
Pepper

## *Method*

- Presoak and cook the beans. Drain and reserve the liquid.
- Fry the carrots, onion, garlic, ginger, courgettes, pepper, cauliflower, mushrooms and peas in the oil until softening.
- Add the mace, cumin, coriander, tumeric and cardamom and fry for one minute more.
- Make the bean water up to 1 pint (500 ml) with water and add to the pan with the stock cube, tomato puree, pickle, mustard, tabasco and pepper. Bring to the boil, cover and simmer on a low heat for 40 minutes until the vegetables are cooked and the liquid has thickened.
- Meanwhile cook the pasta in boiling water with a drop of oil added for 10 minutes or according to the instructions on the packet. Drain.
- Stir the pasta and cooked beans into the spicy sauce, reheat to serving temperature and serve immediately. Good with green salad but can be eaten alone for a filling nutritious dish.

- Freeze in plastic containers and use within 6 weeks.

**Green Lentil Spaghetti**

This tasty sauce can be used with any kind of pasta but is particularly good with wholewheat or buckwheat spaghetti. Brown or red lentils can be used in place of the green ones if preferred.

    8 oz (225 g) green lentils, washed thoroughly
    1 large onion, chopped
    2 cloves garlic, crushed
    1 red or green pepper, sliced
    4 oz (100 g) mushrooms, sliced
    1 tablespoon oil
    1 medium tin tomatoes, liquidized or chopped
    2 tablespoons tomato purée
    1 pint (500 ml) stock
    2 teaspoons basil
    1 tablespoon fresh chopped parsley
    Pepper

*Method*

- Fry the onion, garlic, pepper and mushrooms in the oil for a few minutes.
- Add the lentils, tomatoes, tomato purée, stock, basil and pepper. Bring to the boil, cover and simmer on a low heat for 20–25 minutes until the lentils are cooked and the sauce is thick.
- Add the parsley and simmer for a further 5 minutes. (Add a drop more stock if the sauce seems dry).
- Serve with spaghetti (allowing 3 oz/75 g per person) cooked in boiling water with a drop of oil added for 12 minutes (or according to instructions on packet).
- The sauce can be frozen in plastic containers then thawed and reheated. Cook spaghetti fresh.

**Walnut and Mushroom Tagliatelle**

A delicious, rich mixture of walnuts and mushrooms in a creamy sauce goes particularly well with tagliatelle but any pasta may be used if this is not available.

 2 oz (50 g) margarine
 2 onions, chopped
 2 cloves garlic, crushed
 12 oz (350 g) mushrooms, sliced
 4 sticks celery, chopped
 2 oz (50 g) flour
 1 pint (500 ml) soya milk
 2 teaspoons tarragon
 1 stock cube
 4 oz (100 g) chopped walnuts
 12 oz (350 g) spinach tagliatelle (or other pasta)
 Pepper

*Method*

• Fry the onions, garlic, mushrooms and celery in the margarine
until softening.
• Stir in the flour and cook for one minute.
• *Remove from heat* and stir in the soya milk gradually to avoid
lumps. Add the tarragon, stock cube and pepper.
• Return to a low heat and stir until the sauce has thickened. Stir
in the walnuts.
• Cook the tagliatelle in boiling water with a drop of oil added
for 10 minutes or according to instructions on packet. Drain.
• Stir the cooked tagliatelle into the sauce and reheat gently to
serving temperature. Serve with a green salad.
• Freeze in plastic containers, thaw and reheat in a pan adding
more soya milk if necessary.

**Stir-fry Tofu and Vegetables with Pasta**

This delicious crunchy dish is ideal for whole wheat or buckwheat spaghetti or noodles. It is a variation of a popular
Chinese dish called 'Lo Mein'. Very quick to make.

 8 oz (225 g) spaghetti or noodles broken into 3″ (7 cm)
 lengths
 1 tablespoon olive, sesame or soya oil
 2 carrots, cut into *thin* matchsticks
 1 onion, *thinly* sliced
 4 oz (100 g) cauliflower florets, broken into small pieces
 1 red pepper, cut into *thin* strips

193

4 oz (100 g) mushrooms, sliced
4 oz (100 g) mangetout peas, topped and tailed
2 courgettes, cut into *thin* matchsticks
2 sticks celery, *thinly* sliced
Knob fresh ginger, peeled and grated
2 cloves garlic, crushed
12 oz (350 g) *firm* tofu, drained and cut into *thin* strips
3 tablespoons tamari soy sauce
1 teaspoon coriander
Pepper

## Method

• Cook the pasta in boiling water with a drop of oil added for 10 minutes or according to instructions on packet. Drain. Chop all the vegetables *very thinly* (they will only be cooked for 5 minutes).
• Heat the oil in a wok or large saucepan until nearly smoking.
• Tip in the vegetables, ginger and garlic and toss in the hot oil for 3 minutes.
• Add the tofu and toss for 1 minute.
• Add the soy sauce, coriander, pepper and cooked pasta. Toss for 1 minute then cover and steam for 1 minute. Serve immediately.
• Not suitable for freezing.

## Smoked Tofu and Pasta Savoury

Smoked tofu cubes give an interesting flavour and added nutritive value to this creamy tomato sauce. Any pasta can be used but shells, twists or macaroni are particularly nice.

2 tablespoons olive oil
1 small aubergine, cut into chunky pieces
8 oz (225 g) cauliflower florets, broken into small pieces
2 sticks celery, chopped
1 onion, chopped
2 cloves garlic, crushed
1 red pepper, sliced
2 heaped tablespoons flour
1 pint (500 ml) soya milk

8 oz (225 g) smoked tofu, drained and cut into small cubes
2 tablespoons tomato purée
2 tablespoons fresh chopped parsley
2 teaspoons oregano
8 oz (225 g) wholewheat pasta (e.g. shells, twists, macaroni)
Pepper

## Method

• Fry the aubergine, cauliflower, celery, onion, garlic and pepper in the oil until softening. Cover and allow to 'sweat' for 5 minutes.
• Stir in the flour and cook for one minute.
• *Remove from heat* and add the soya milk gradually, stirring continuously to avoid lumps. Add the tomato puree, parsley, oregano, pepper and tofu cubes.
• Return to a low heat and stir until thickened.
• Cook the pasta in boiling water with a drop of oil added for 10 minutes or according to instructions on packet. Drain and add to the sauce. Bring to serving temperature and serve immediately.
• Can be eaten alone or with a crisp salad.
• Freeze the sauce in plastic containers, thaw and reheat, adding a drop more soya milk if necessary. Cook the pasta fresh and stir in.

## Haricot and Macaroni Bake

This tasty bake with its crispy topping is extremely nutritious. Any beans or pasta may be substituted for the haricot beans and macaroni for a change.

4 oz (100 g) haricot beans
4 oz (100 g) wholewheat macaroni
1 tablespoon olive oil
2 onions, chopped
2 cloves garlic, crushed
2 sticks celery, chopped
2 courgettes, chopped
4 oz (100 g) mushrooms, sliced
1 medium tin tomatoes, chopped or liquidized

2 tablespoon tomato purée
2 teaspoon basil
Pepper

*Topping*
4 oz (100 g) wholemeal breadcrumbs
2 oz (50 g) ground hazelnuts or cashew nuts
2 oz (50 g) margarine
1 tablespoon fresh chopped parsley

### Method

Set the oven to Gas 5/190°C/375°F.
Grease a 3 pint (1½ litre) ovenproof dish or baking tin.

- Presoak and cook the beans as described on page 95. Drain and reserve liquid.
- Fry the onions, garlic, celery, courgettes and mushrooms in the oil until softening.
- Add the tomatoes, tomato purée, basil, pepper and ¼ pint (150 ml) reserved liquid. Bring to the boil, cover and simmer on a low heat for 15 minutes until the vegetables are soft and the liquid has thickened.
- Meanwhile cook the macaroni in boiling water with a drop of oil added for 8 minutes so it is slightly undercooked. Drain.
- Mix the macaroni, beans and tomato sauce together and pour into the prepared dish. (The mixture should be fairly moist as the macaroni will absorb a lot of liquid during baking).
- Melt the margarine and stir in the breadcrumbs, nuts and parsley. Sprinkle this mixture over the top of the macaroni base.
- Bake for 30 minutes until brown and crispy on top. Serve with a green salad.
- Freeze unbaked, thaw and bake as described.

### Cashew Nut and Vegetable Spaghetti

This creamy sauce can be used with any kind of pasta but is especially good with wholewheat, spinach or buckwheat spaghetti. Very quick and easy to make.

2 oz (50 g) margarine
1 onion, chopped
2 cloves garlic, crushed

4 oz (100 g) mushrooms, sliced
1 red pepper, sliced
4 courgettes, sliced
8 oz (225 g) frozen or tinned sweetcorn
2 oz (50 g) flour
1 pint (500 ml) soya milk
2 teaspoons coriander
2 tablespoons parsley
2 teaspoons miso
1 tablespoon tahini
4 oz (100 g) cashew nuts
Pepper

## Method

• Fry the onion, garlic, mushrooms, pepper, courgettes and sweetcorn in the margarine until softening. Cover and allow to 'sweat' for 5 minutes.

• Stir in the flour and cook for one minute.

• *Remove from heat* and stir in the soya milk gradually, stirring continuously to avoid lumps. Add the coriander, parsley, tahini, pepper and cashew nuts.

• Return to a low heat and stir until the sauce has thickened. Add miso and stir until it has dissolved but *do not boil* or the beneficial enzymes in the miso will be destroyed.

• Serve immediately with spaghetti (allowing 3 oz/75 g per person) cooked in boiling water with a drop of oil added for 12 minutes (or according to instructions on packet).

• The sauce can be frozen in plastic containers then thawed and reheated, adding a little more soya milk if necessary. Cook spaghetti fresh.

I have used *miso* in a lot of my casseroles because it gives a superb savoury flavour and is also very nutritious. It should be added near the end of cooking time (usually dissolved in warm water) but *never boiled* or the beneficial enzymes it contains will be destroyed. I use *mugi miso* (soya and barley) as it is not so strong as some of the others but feel free to use any variety. Miso is fairly expensive but lasts for ages and is well worth the investment for the results it gives. However if you feel you cannot afford miso, use yeast extract instead but reduce the quantity slightly as it has a stronger flavour.

For more information on miso see pp. 98, 108.

### Vegetable and Barley Stew with Coriander

A hearty winter stew tinged with the subtle flavour of ground coriander seeds. A welcoming dish on a cold day!

> 2 lb (900 g) root vegetables, diced e.g. potato, turnip, carrot, parsnip, swede, artichokes, kohlrabi, beetroot etc.
> 1 onion, chopped
> 2 cloves garlic, crushed
> 2 tablespoons oil
> 6 oz (175 g) pot barley, washed
> 2 pints (1 litre) stock
> 2 tablespoons tomato purée
> 4 teaspoons coriander seeds
> 2 tablespoons fresh chopped parsley

2 teaspoons miso
Pepper

### Method

• Fry the root vegetables, onion and garlic in the oil for a few minutes.
• Add the pot barley, stock, tomato purée, parsley and pepper. Crush the coriander seeds in a pestle-and-mortar (or in a bowl with a rolling pin) and add to the stew.
• Bring to the boil, cover and simmer on a low heat for 45 minutes, stirring occasionally, until the barley is cooked and the liquid thickened.
• Dissolve the miso in ¼ pint (150 ml) warm water and add to the stew. Bring to serving temperature but *do not boil* or the beneficial enzymes in the miso will be destroyed.
• Serve with crusty wholemeal bread or jacket potatoes. In order to achieve protein complementarity the stew should be served with a nut or pulse dish. This is easily achieved by serving with a tofu sweet, a nutty sponge pudding or a pudding with some tofu cream on it for example.
• Freeze in plastic boxes, thaw and reheat gently in a pan.


## Rooty Lentil Stew

A thick tasty stew of seasonal root vegetables and red lentils. A real winter warmer!

2 lb (900 g) diced root vegetables (e.g. potatoes, beet-root, parsnip, swede, Jerusalem artichokes, turnip, celeriac, carrots etc.)
1 large onion, chopped
2 cloves garlic, crushed
Knob margarine
8 oz (225 g) red lentils, washed thoroughly
Medium tin tomatoes, chopped
1½ pints (775 ml) strong stock
3 bayleaves
2 teaspoons mixed herbs
1 heaped tablespoon tomato purée
Black pepper
2 teaspoons miso

*Method*

• Fry the onion and garlic in the margarine for a few minutes. Add the root vegetables and fry for a further 2–3 minutes.

• Add the stock, tinned tomatoes, bayleaves, tomato puree, herbs and pepper. Bring to the boil and simmer, covered for 20 minutes.

• Add the lentils and simmer for another 15 minutes, stirring occasionally until the lentils are cooked.

• Dissolve the miso in $\frac{1}{4}$ pint (150 ml) *warm* water and add to the hot-pot. Stir well and bring to serving temperature. *Do not boil* or the enzymes in the miso will be destroyed.

• If miso is not available yeast extract can be used.

• Serve with chunks of wholemeal bread or rolls to achieve protein complementarity and provide a nutritious, filling meal

• Freezes well in plastic containers.


**Bean and Vegetable Stew**

A thick tasty mixture of seasonal vegetables and kidney beans. Serve with chunks of wholemeal bread for a nutritious, warming meal.

6 oz (175 g) red kidney beans
1 large onion, chopped
2 cloves garlic, crushed
1$\frac{1}{2}$ lb (725 g) diced vegetables (e.g. potato, celeriac, parsnip, beetroot, carrots, courgettes, celery, turnip, swede, aubergine, peppers, cauliflower, leeks)
2 tablespoons oil
1 stock cube
2 teaspoons mixed herbs
2 bayleaves
2 tablespoons tomato purée
2 teaspoons miso
Black pepper

*Method*

• Presoak and cook the kidney beans. Drain and reserve liquid.

• Fry the vegetables, onion and garlic in the oil for 5 minutes until softening.

- Make the bean water up to 1 pint (500 ml) and add to the vegetables with the stock cube, tomato purée, herbs and bayleaf. Season well with pepper.
- Bring to the boil then cover and simmer on a low heat for 20 minutes until the vegetables are cooked.
- Add the cooked beans and simmer uncovered, for a further 20 minutes to reduce the liquid.
- Dissolve the miso in $\frac{1}{4}$ pint (150 ml) *warm* water and add to the stew. Bring to serving temperature but *do not boil* or the beneficial enzymes in the miso will be destroyed.
- If miso is not available, yeast extract may be used.
- Serve with wholemeal bread or cooked grains to achieve protein complementarity. Allow 3 oz (75 g) dry weight grain per person.
- Freezes well in plastic containers.


## Pinto Bean, Fennel and Okra Casserole

This combination of exotic flavours and textures makes this dish very unusual and tasty. No thickening agent is required as the okra are a natural thickener.

4 oz (100 g) pinto beans
2 tablespoons oil
2 onions, chopped
2 cloves garlic, crushed
2 heads fennel, chopped in chunky pieces
4 carrots, diced
1 red pepper, sliced
8 oz (225 g) okra, washed
1 stock cube
2 tablespoons fresh chopped parsley
2 teaspoons tarragon
4 tablespoons tomato purée
Pepper

*Method*

- Presoak and cook the beans. Drain and reserve liquid.
- Fry the onions, garlic, fennel, carrots and pepper in the oil for a few minutes until softening.
- Make the reserved liquid up to 1$\frac{1}{2}$ pints (775 ml) and add

to the vegetables with the stock cube, parsley, tarragon and tomato purée.

• Top and tail the okra and chop into chunky pieces. Add to the casserole and season well. Bring to the boil, cover and simmer for 15 minutes.

• Add the pinto beans and simmer for another 10 minutes until thick and the vegetables are cooked.

• Serve with wholemeal bread or cooked grain to achieve protein complementarity. Allow 3 oz (75 g) dry weight grain per person.

• Freeze in plastic containers, thaw and reheat gently adding more stock if necessary.


**Tofu and Tahini Casserole**

A delicious, rich tahini sauce is an ideal way to make tofu tasty. The slightly sweet flavour provided by the fruit in the recipe seems to complement the sauce particularly well.

> 2 tablespoons oil
> 2 onions, chopped
> 2 cloves garlic, crushed
> 2 small cooking apples, peeled, cored and chopped
> 4 oz (100 g) fresh or tinned (unsweetened) pineapple cut into small cubes
> 1 green pepper, sliced
> 4 oz (100 g) mushrooms, sliced
> 2 sticks celery, chopped
> 1 pint (500 ml) stock
> 1 tablespoon tamari soy sauce
> $\frac{1}{2}$ teaspoon nutmeg
> 1 teaspoon ground cardamom
> 8 oz (225 g) *firm* tofu, drained and cubed
> 4 tablespoons tahini
> 2 tablespoons fresh chopped parsley
> Pepper

*Method*

• Fry the onions, garlic, apple, pineapple, pepper, mushrooms and celery in the oil for a few minutes until softening.

• Add the stock, soy sauce, nutmeg, cardamom and pepper. Bring to the boil, cover and simmer on a low heat for 20 minutes

until the vegetables are soft.
- Add the tofu cubes and simmer uncovered for a further 10 minutes.
- Add the tahini and parsley, stir until the tahini has dissolved, then cook on a low heat for 5 minutes until the sauce has thickened.
- Serve with wholemeal bread, jacket potatoes or cooked grain (allowing 3 oz/75 g dry weight per person).
- Not suitable for freezing.

**Spiced Kidney Bean Casserole**

This lightly spiced casserole is a very quick and easy way to make kidney beans into a tasty dish. Serve with wholemeal bread or cooked grain to achieve protein complementarity.

> 8 oz (225 g) red or brown kidney beans
> 2 onions, chopped
> 4 cloves garlic, crushed
> 2 tablespoons olive oil
> 2 medium tins tomatoes, chopped
> $\frac{1}{4}$ pint (150 ml) stock
> 2 tablespoons tomato purée
> 2 teaspoons cumin
> 2 teaspoons coriander
> Rind 1 small lemon
> $\frac{1}{2}$ teaspoon ground mace
> 2 tablespoons fresh chopped parsley
> Pepper

*Method*

Set oven to Gas 4/180°C/350°F.

- Presoak and cook the beans. Drain.
- Fry the onions and garlic in the oil until softening. Place in a 4 pint (2 litre) ovenproof casserole dish with the cooked beans, tomatoes, stock, tomato purée, cumin, coriander, lemon rind, mace, parsley and pepper.
- Cover and bake in the centre of the oven for 1 hour until the casserole has thickened.
- Serve with wholemeal bread or cooked grain (allowing 3 oz/75 g dry weight per person).

• Freeze in plastic containers, thaw and reheat gently in a pan.

## Chick Pea and Aubergine Goulash

A lightly spiced, rich sauce that goes well with rice, bulgar, couscous or jacket potatoes to make a nutritious, filling meal.

6 oz (175 g) chick peas
2 onions, chopped
2 cloves garlic, crushed
2 large aubergines, cut in chunky pieces
1 large red pepper, sliced
2 tablespoons olive oil
1 medium tin tomatoes, liquidized or chopped
3 tablespoons tomato purée
2 teaspoons carraway seeds
1 tablespoonful paprika
1 teaspoon mace
1 teaspoon cayenne pepper
2 tablespoons chopped fresh parsley
1 stock cube or 1 teaspoon stock concentrate
Black pepper

*Method*

• Presoak and cook the chick peas. Drain and reserve liquid.
• Fry the onion, garlic, aubergine and pepper in the oil until softening. Cover and allow to 'sweat' for 5 minutes.
• Put the carraway seeds into a saucepan or frying pan and toast on a low heat until the seeds begin to 'pop' and jump around. Stir regularly to prevent burning.
• Make the chickpea reserved liquid up to 1 pint (500 ml) and add to the vegetables with the stock cube or concentrate, toasted carraway seeds, tomatoes, tomato purée, paprika, mace, cayenne pepper, parsley and black pepper.
• Bring to the boil then reduce the heat, cover and simmer for 15 minutes until the vegetables are cooked and the liquid is thickened. Stir occasionally.
• Add the cooked chickpeas and simmer for a further 5 minutes.
• Serve with bread or cooked grain to achieve protein complementarity and a crisp salad. Allow 3 oz (75 g) dry weight of grain per person.

*Note*: *If the goulash is to be served with potatoes, a grain salad or sweet made from pastry should be served with it to complete the protein content of the meal.*
- Freezes well in plastic containers but use within 6 weeks.


### Lentil Hot-pot

A very simple baked hot-pot that requires no attention once it is in the oven. Very popular with children.

> 8 oz (225 g) red lentils, washed thoroughly
> 2 onions, chopped
> 2 cloves garlic, crushed
> 1 red pepper, sliced
> 1 head fennel, chopped
> 2 sticks celery, chopped
> 4 oz (100 g) mushrooms, sliced
> 1 tablespoon oil
> 2 tablespoons fresh chopped parsley
> 2 teaspoons thyme
> 1 lb (450 g) potatoes, scrubbed (but not peeled)
> $\frac{3}{4}$ pint (450 ml) stock
> 1 teaspoonful miso
> 1 oz (25 g) margarine
> Pepper

*Method*

Set oven to Gas 4/180°C/350°F.
Grease a 2 pint (1 litre) ovenproof dish.

- Fry the onions, garlic, pepper, fennel, celery and mushrooms in the oil until softening.
- Layer the fried vegetables and lentils in the prepared dish, starting and finishing with a vegetable layer and sprinkling each layer with some of the parsley, thyme and pepper.
- Slice the potatoes thinly and lay on top of the hot-pot.
- Warm the stock and dissolve the miso in it. Pour over the hot-pot (it should completely cover the lentils and vegetables). Dot the margarine on top of the potatoes.
- Cover and bake for 1 hour, removing the lid for the last 15 minutes to brown the potatoes.
- Serve with steamed green vegetables. In order to achieve

protein complementarity the hot-pot should be served with a grain dish. This is easily achieved by serving a pastry-based sweet.

## Pinto Bean, Aubergine and Mushroom Casserole

A rich, tasty casserole which is very easy to prepare. Serve it with bread, rice or other grain to achieve protein complementarity.

    8 oz (225 g) pinto beans — soaked overnight
    8 oz (225 g) mushrooms, sliced
    2 onions, chopped
    2 cloves garlic, crushed
    2 aubergines, chopped in chunky pieces
    4 tablespoons olive oil
    2 teaspoons basil
    2 tablespoons fresh chopped parsley
    1 medium tin tomatoes, chopped
    1 pint (500 ml) stock
    2 tablespoons tomato purée
    2 teaspoons miso
    Pepper

*Method*

Set oven to Gas 4/180°C/350°F.

• Fry the onion, garlic, mushrooms and aubergine in the oil until softening.
• Pour into a 4 pint (2 litre) ovenproof casserole dish and add the soaked beans, basil, parsley, tomatoes, tomato puree and pepper.
• Warm the stock on a *low heat* and add the miso. Stir until the miso has dissolved then add the stock to the casserole.
• Stir well to mix all the ingredients, cover and bake in the centre of the oven for 1½ hours until the beans are soft and the liquid thickened.
• Adjust seasoning and serve with bread, rice or cooked grains (allowing 3 oz/75 g dry weight per person).
• Freeze in plastic containers, thaw and reheat gently in a pan.

## Red Bean Chilli

A very popular dish. My chilli is quite mild as I personally do not like my food too hot so if you are one of those people who likes to sweat when you eat chilli you will need to double the quantity of spices I have given below!

8 oz (225 g) red kidney beans
2 tablespoons olive oil
1 aubergine, chopped
1 onion, chopped
1 red pepper, chopped
2 cloves garlic, crushed
4 oz (100 g) mushrooms, sliced
1 stock cube
1 medium tin tomatoes, liquidized or chopped
2 tablespoons tomato purée
$\frac{1}{4}$ teaspoon chilli powder
$\frac{1}{4}$ teaspoon tabasco sauce
4 teaspoons paprika
$\frac{1}{4}$ teaspoon cayenne pepper

### Method

- Presoak and cook the beans. Drain and reserve liquid.
- Fry the aubergine, onion, pepper, garlic and mushrooms in the oil until softening. Cover and 'sweat' for 5 minutes.
- Make the reserved liquid up to 1 pint (500 ml) and add to the pan with the stock cube, tinned tomatoes, tomato purée, chilli powder, tabasco, paprika and cayenne. Bring to the boil, cover and simmer on a low heat for 20 minutes until the liquid has thickened.
- Add the cooked beans and simmer uncovered for a further 10 minutes.
- Serve with rice, bulgar, pasta or other cooked grains to achieve protein complementarity. Allow 3 oz (75 g) dry weight of grain per person.
- Freeze in plastic containers and use within 6 weeks.

## Pinto Bean and Wheatberry Casserole

This cheap, tasty stew of beans, wheatberries and root

vegetables has a lovely texture and is particularly nutritious. Lovely as a warming main course on a cold winters day.

4 oz (100 g) pinto beans
2 oz (50 g) wheatberries (whole wheat)
2 onions, chopped
2 cloves garlic, crushed
1½ lb (675 g) root vegetables diced (e.g. potato, carrot, swede, parsnip, turnip, kohlrabi, celeriac, artichokes etc.)
2 tablespoons oil
2 medium tins tomatoes, chopped or liquidized
1 stock cube
2 bay leaves
2 teaspoons basil
Pepper
2 teaspoons miso

### Method

- Presoak and cook the pinto beans. Drain and reserve liquid.
- Boil the wheatberries until soft. Drain.
- Fry the onion, garlic and root vegetables in the oil until softening.
- Add the tinned tomatoes, bayleaves, basil and stock cube. Make the reserved bean liquid up to 1 pint (500 ml) and add. Stir well.
- Bring to the boil, cover and simmer on a low heat for 40 minutes until the vegetables are cooked.
- Add the cooked beans and wheatberries, season with pepper and simmer for a further 15 minutes until thickened.
- Dissolve the miso in ¼ pint (150 ml) water and stir in. Bring to serving temperature but *do not boil* or the beneficial enzymes in the miso will be destroyed.
- Serve with wholemeal bread or jacket potatoes.
- Freeze in plastic containers, thaw and reheat gently.

## Root Vegetables and Cashews in Parsnip Sauce

This unusual dish is an interesting way to make the most of delicious winter vegetables. Served with salad or green vegetables, it makes a hearty, filling meal. *This recipe is dedicated to Stasha.*

8 oz (225 g) parsnips, scrubbed
2 lb (900 g) root vegetables scrubbed (or peeled where necessary) and cut into chunky pieces e.g. carrots, potatoes, celeriac, turnip, swede, Jerusalem artichokes
1 onion, chopped
1 clove garlic, crushed
1 tablespoon oil
4 oz (100 g) cashew nuts
$\frac{3}{4}$ pint (450 ml) soya milk
1 oz (25 g) wholemeal flour
1 oz (25 g) margarine
2 tablespoons fresh chopped parsley
1 teaspoon mace powder
1 teaspoon coriander
Black pepper

*Method*

Set oven to Gas 4/180°C/350°F.
Grease a 3 pint (1½ litre) ovenproof dish.

• Chop the parsnips and remove any woody core. Boil in water until tender and drain.
• Put the cooked parsnips and the soya milk into a liquidizer and blend until smooth.
• Put the parsnip purée, flour, margarine, mace, coriander, parsley and pepper into a pan and whisk on a low heat until the sauce has thickened and is boiling. Put to one side.
• Steam or pressure cook the root vegetables in the minimum amount of water until just cooked. Drain.
• Fry the onion and garlic in the oil until softening.
• Combine the onion and garlic, cooked root vegetables, parsnip sauce and cashew nuts in a bowl and mix thoroughly, seasoning to taste with black pepper.
• Pour into the prepared dish, cover with foil and reheat for 15–20 minutes.
• The parsnip sauce can be frozen in plastic boxes and reheated after thawing to serve. Cook the vegetables fresh and stir in, adding a little more milk if necessary.

**Chickpeas and Vegetables in Tahini Sauce**

This rich, creamy dish is an adaptation of a Mexican recipe. It is very nutritious and can be served on its own with wholemeal

209

bread or with cooked grain (rice, bulgar, couscous etc.) to make a substantial meal.

4 oz (100 g) chickpeas
2 tablespoons olive oil
Knob fresh ginger, peeled and grated
2 cloves garlic, crushed
1 large aubergine, cut into chunky cubes
2 onions, chopped
4 oz (100 g) mushrooms, sliced
1 lb (500 g) courgettes, chopped
4 oz (100 g) cauliflower florets, broken into small pieces
1 small head of fennel, chopped
2 teaspoons wholegrain mustard
$\frac{1}{2}$ teaspoon cayenne pepper
1 teaspoon turmeric
2 teaspoons cumin
2 teaspoons coriander
1 medium tin tomatoes, liquidized or chopped
1 tablespoon soy sauce
1 tablespoon tomato purée
1 stock cube
Juice 1 lemon
2 tablespoons tahini (sesame paste)
2 tablespoons water
Black pepper

### Method

- Presoak and cook the chickpeas. Drain and reserve the liquid.
- Fry the ginger, garlic, aubergine, onion, mushrooms, courgettes, cauliflower and fennel in the olive oil until softening. Cover and allow to 'sweat' for 5 minutes.
- Stir in the mustard, cayenne, turmeric, cumin and coriander and fry for a further minute.
- Add the tinned tomatoes, tomato purée, soy sauce, stock cube and $\frac{1}{2}$ pint (275 ml) chickpea reserved liquid. Bring to the boil, cover and simmer for 10 minutes until the vegetables are soft.
- Mix the tahini with the water and lemon juice to form a smooth cream. Season well with black pepper.
- Add the cooked chickpeas and tahini cream to the veget-

ables. Stir well and reheat to serving temperature.

• Serve with bread or cooked grain, allowing 3 oz (75 g) dry weight per person.

• For freezing, leave the tahini cream out of the recipe and add after thawing.

• For entertaining purposes this dish is even more delicious if made the day before it is required and allowed to stand in the refrigerator overnight.

CURRIES
RICE
DISHES

As you will see from the curry recipes they all have extremely long lists of ingredients which can be quite daunting! Don't be put off however, as they are all very simple to make. The reason for the long lists in most cases is because of the variety of spices used. Authentic tasting Indian spices combined with fresh root ginger, produce a much milder and more aromatic curry than plain curry powder on its own.

If you particularly like curries, I would strongly recommend you to buy some fresh root ginger and the basic spices I have listed below. You may also want to purchase some solid coconut cream which really does add a superior flavour — Sharwoods is a particularly good brand. If you are not fond of curries and only make them occasionally, then just buy a good quality curry powder (Sharwoods is very good) and substitute this for the spices I have used.

All the spices listed below are cheaper bought loose from health food shops, Indian shops and delicatessens but may also be obtainable from supermarkets. For more information on spices see pp. 110–114.

| Basic curry spices | Other useful curry ingredients |
| --- | --- |
| Coriander | Fresh root ginger |
| Cumin | Solid coconut cream |
| Cardamom | Indian pickle (sweet or hot) |
| Turmeric | Wholegrain mustard |
| Garam masala | Chutney |

# Mild Lentil Curry and Rice

A mild, aromatic curry suitable for red, brown or green lentils or split peas. I prefer red lentils as they cook more quickly and give a smoother texture. The curry can be made stronger by increasing the quantities of spices used.

Knob margarine
1 large onion, chopped
2 cloves garlic, crushed
1 knob fresh ginger, peeled and grated
1 pepper, chopped
1 small aubergine, chopped
4 sticks celery, sliced
4 oz (100 g) mushrooms, sliced
12 oz (350 g) red lentils, washed thoroughly
1½ pints (775 ml) stock
Medium tin tomatoes, chopped
1 tablespoon tomato purée
1 tablespoon pickle
2 teaspoons wholegrain mustard
4 teaspoons curry powder
4 teaspoons cumin
4 teaspoons coriander
2 teaspoons ground cardamom
2 teaspoons turmeric
2 teaspoons garam masala
Black pepper
Brown rice to serve – allow 3 oz (75 g) per person.

## Method

• Fry the onion, garlic and ginger in the margarine for a few minutes until softening.
• Add the pepper, aubergine, celery and mushrooms. Stir to coat in margarine then add the curry spices except the garam masala and fry for 2–3 minutes.
• Add the lentils, stock, tomatoes, tomato purée, pickle, mustard and pepper. Bring to the boil then simmer, covered, for 20–25 minutes until the lentils are cooked and the curry is thick. (If brown or green lentils are used this will probably take 30 minutes and split peas may take up to 45 minutes).
• Add the garam masala and simmer for another 5 minutes.
• Serve with rice, sliced banana or coconut.

- The curry will freeze but should be eaten within 6 weeks because of the spices it contains which will intensify in flavour if kept too long.

## Sweet Vegetable Curry and Rice

This mild, sweet curry is an excellent way to use up left over vegetables. The sweetness can be reduced if preferred by omitting the coconut, sultanas and apple. As with all curries the flavour is greatly improved if it is made the day before required.

> 2 lb (900 g) diced root vegetables e.g. potato, swede, carrot, parsnip, turnip, Jerusalem artichokes, celeriac, beetroot etc.
> 1 large onion, chopped
> 2 cloves garlic, crushed
> Knob margarine
> 1 large cooking apple, peeled, cored and chopped
> 1 tablespoon dessicated coconut or 1 oz (25 g) solid coconut cream (e.g. Sharwoods)
> 1 tablespoon tomato purée
> 1 tablespoon sultanas
> 1 tablespoon pickle or chutney
> 2 teaspoons curry powder
> $\frac{1}{2}$ teaspoon cayenne pepper
> 1 teaspoon cumin
> 2 teaspoons coriander
> 2 teaspoons ground cardamom
> 2 teaspoons turmeric
> 1 teaspoon garam masala
> 1 pint ($\frac{1}{2}$ litre) stock
> Brown rice to serve — allow 3 oz (75 g) per person

### Method

- Fry the onion and garlic in the knob of margarine for a few minutes. Add the curry spices except the garam masala and continue frying for 2 minutes.
- Add the root vegetables and stir over a low heat for a few minutes to coat the vegetables with spices.
- Add the stock, apple, sultanas, pickle and tomato puree. Bring to the boil then simmer, covered, for 1 hour on a low heat. Stir occasionally.

214

- Add the garam masala and the coconut and simmer for a further 10 minutes, stirring occasionally.
- Serve with hot brown rice, chippatis or popadoms and sliced banana if liked.
- The curry will freeze but should be eaten within 6 weeks because of the spices it contains which will intensify in flavour if kept too long. For freezing, leave the coconut out of the recipe and add after thawing.
- As the curry only contains rice and vegetables it is advisable to serve a nut or bean dish with it to achieve complementarity. This can be done by serving a bean or nut side salad or a tofu dessert.


## Yellow Pea, Cauliflower and Pineapple Curry

This mild curry enhances the flavour of the peas and pineapple which seem to go particularly well together. The cauliflower adds texture and 'eye-appeal' to the golden-coloured sauce.

2 tablespoons oil
2 onions, chopped
2 cloves garlic, crushed
Knob fresh ginger, peeled and grated
1 cooking apple, peeled, cored and chopped
12 oz (350 g) cauliflower florets, broken into chunky pieces
12 oz (350 g) fresh or tinned (unsweetened) pineapple
12 oz (350 g) yellow split peas, washed thoroughly
1½ pints (675 ml) stock
1 medium tin tomatoes, chopped
2 teaspoons cumin
2 teaspoons coriander
4 teaspoons curry powder
2 teaspoons turmeric
2 teaspoons garam masala
2 teaspoons pickle
2 teaspoons wholegrain mustard
Pepper
Brown rice to serve — allow 3 oz (75 g) per person

- Fry the onion, garlic, ginger, apple, cauliflower and pineapple in the oil until softening.

215

- Stir in the cumin, coriander, curry powder and turmeric. Fry for one minute.
- Add the split peas, stock, tinned tomatoes, mustard, pickle and pepper. Bring to the boil then cover and simmer on a low heat for 45 minutes until the peas are cooked and the liquid is absorbed.
- Stir in the garam masala and simmer for a further 5 minutes before serving with dessicated coconut and banana slices.
- The curry will freeze but use within 6 weeks because the spices intensify in flavour after this time.

## Fruit and Beansprout Curry

This beautiful fruity curry is one of my personal favourites. It has a mild but piquant flavour and is lovely and thick. The strength can be increased by doubling the quantities of spices used if desired.

2 tablespoons oil
2 onions, chopped
2 cloves garlic, crushed
Knob fresh ginger, peeled and grated
2 sticks celery, chopped
1 small aubergine, chopped
8 oz (225 g) mung bean or lentil sprouts
4 oz (100 g) dried apricots, chopped
1 small cooking apple, peeled, cored and chopped
4 oz (100 g) raisins
1 ripe banana, sliced
1 pint (500 ml) stock
2 tablespoons tomato purée
2 teaspoons sweet pickle
2 teaspoons wholegrain mustard
2 teaspoons cumin
4 teaspoons coriander
2 teaspoons ground cardamom
2 teaspoons curry powder
2 teaspoons turmeric
1 teaspoon mace
2 teaspoons garam masala
2 oz (50 g) solid coconut cream (e.g. *Sharwoods*)
Pepper

Brown rice to serve — allow 3 oz (75 g) per person

### Method

• Fry the onion, garlic, ginger, celery and aubergine in the oil for a few minutes.
• Stir in all the spices (except the garam masala) and fry for one minute.
• Add the stock, mustard, pickle, tomato puree, apricots, apple, raisins, banana and pepper. Bring to the boil, cover and simmer on a low heat for 20 minutes until the vegetables are cooked and the liquid thickened.
• Add the beansprouts, garam masala and coconut cream. Stir over a low heat for 5 minutes until the coconut cream has melted. Serve immediately with rice.
• The curry will freeze, but leave the coconut cream out of the recipe and use within 6 weeks. Add the coconut cream after thawing.

## Tofu, Bean or Cashew Curry and Rice

This is a fairly strong, aromatic curry base, suitable for currying tofu cubes, cooked beans or cashew nuts. The strength can be reduced by halving the quantities of spices used if preferred.

12 oz (350 g) firm tofu cubes, cooked beans or cashew nuts
2 tablespoons oil
1 large onion, chopped
2 cloves garlic, crushed
Knob fresh ginger, grated
3 sticks celery, chopped
3 carrots, chopped
1 green pepper, sliced
4 oz (100 g) mushrooms, sliced
Medium tin tomatoes, chopped
1 pint (500 ml) stock
1 tablespoon pickle or chutney
2 teaspoons wholegrain mustard
2 teaspoons curry powder
4 teaspoons cumin

4 teaspoons coriander
2 teaspoons ground cardamom
2 teaspoons turmeric
½ teaspoon nutmeg
2 teaspoons garam masala
Pepper
2 oz (50 g) solid coconut cream (optional)
Brown rice to serve — allow 3 oz (75 g) per person

## *Method*

- Fry the onion, garlic and ginger in the oil for a few minutes until softening.
- Add the curry spices (except garam masala) and fry for 1 minute, stirring.
- Add the celery, carrots, pepper, mushrooms, tomatoes, stock, pickle and mustard. Season with pepper. Bring to the boil, then reduce heat and simmer for 40 minutes covered, stirring occasionally.
- Uncover and simmer for another 10 minutes to reduce the liquid and thicken the curry slightly.
- Add the garam masala and the tofu, beans or cashews. Stir well then simmer for another 10 minutes uncovered.
- Stir in the coconut cream (if using) allow it to melt, then bring to serving temperature and serve with brown rice, pitta bread or chippatis.
- The curry will freeze but leave out the coconut cream and eat within 6 weeks because the spices will intensify in flavour if kept too long.

## Fruity Adzuki Risotto

This rich, tropical flavoured risotto can be made with any type of beans but adzukis are a particularly nutritious combination with rice often used in Eastern dishes and Macrobiotic cookery.

4 oz (100 g) adzuki beans
12 oz (350 g) long grain brown rice, washed thoroughly
1 large onion, sliced
2 cloves garlic, crushed
Knob fresh ginger, peeled and grated
2 courgettes, sliced

4 oz (100 g) mushrooms, sliced
1 red pepper, sliced
2 tablespoons oil
6 oz (175 g) fresh or tinned (unsweetened) pineapple, cubed
2 oz (50 g) raisins or sultanas
1 stock cube
2 tablespoons soy sauce
1 teaspoon coriander
1 teaspoon ground cardamom
Black pepper

## Method

• Presoak and cook the beans. Drain and reserve liquid.
• Fry the onion, garlic, ginger, courgettes, mushrooms, pepper and pineapple in the oil until softening.
• Make the reserved bean liquid up to 1¼ pints (650 ml) and add to the vegetables with the stock cube, rice, raisins or sultanas, soy sauce, coriander, cardamom and pepper. Mix thoroughly.
• Bring to the boil, reduced heat, *cover* and simmer for 30 minutes, stirring occasionally until the rice is nearly cooked and most of the liquid is absorbed.
• Add the cooked adzuki beans and simmer, *uncovered* for a further 15 minutes or until all the liquid has been absorbed.
• Serve with side salad or eat on its own for a filling, nutritious meal.
• Freeze well in plastic boxes but use within 6 weeks.

### Pinto and Aubergine Risotto

A rich tomato-based risotto with a tang of pineapple. Very easy to make. Any beans may be substituted for the pinto beans if they are not available.

4 oz (100 g) pinto beans
12 oz (350 g) long-grain brown rice, washed
1 onion, chopped
2 cloves garlic, crushed
2 sticks celery, chopped
2 medium aubergines, cut in chunky pieces
8 oz (225 g) fresh or tinned (unsweetened) pineapple, cubed

4 tablespoons olive oil
1 medium tin tomatoes, liquidized or chopped
1 stock cube
2 tablespoons tomato purée
2 tablespoons fresh chopped parsley
2 teaspoons basil
1 tablespoon soy sauce
Pepper

## *Method*

- Cook the rice. Drain and rinse to separate grains.
- Presoak and cook the pinto beans. Drain and reserve liquid.
- Fry the onion, garlic, celery, aubergines and pineapple in the oil until softening.
- Add the tomatoes, tomato purée, parsley, basil, soy sauce, stock cube and pepper. Make the reserved bean liquid up to ½ pint (275 ml) and add to the pan. Bring to the boil, cover and simmer on a low heat for 20 minutes. Stir occasionally.
- Add the cooked beans and rice and simmer for a further 10 minutes until all the liquid has been absorbed. Stir regularly to prevent sticking.
- Serve immediately with a green salad.
- Freeze in plastic containers and use within 8 weeks.

## Tofu Stir-Fry with Rice

This crunchy, colourful stir-fry has a very authentic Chinese flavour and is extremely nutritious. It takes a while to prepare but only minutes to cook and is ideal as a dinner party dish because the ingredients can be prepared in advance and fried at the last minute.

8 oz (225 g) *firm* tofu, drained and cut into thin strips
3 tablespoons tamari soy sauce (or shoyu if tamari not available)
1 tablespoon coriander
Black pepper
Knob fresh ginger, peeled and grated
2 cloves garlic, crushed
4 oz (100 g) tinned bamboo shoots (e.g. Lotus Brand), sliced

220

4 oz (100 g) mangetout (Chinese Snow Peas), topped
and tailed
2 large onions, *thinly* sliced
1 red pepper, *thinly* sliced
3 carrots, scrubbed and cut into *thin* 'matchsticks'
6 oz (175 g) mushrooms, *thinly* sliced
8 oz (225 g) mung bean sprouts
8 oz (225 g) brown rice
1 tablespoon soya, sesame or olive oil

## Method

- Cook the rice. Drain and rinse to separate grains.
- Mix the tamari sauce, coriander and pepper together. Place the tofu strips on a shallow plate or saucer and pour the tamari mixture over evenly so all the slices are coated. Stir gently to ensure even coating. Allow to stand for 30 minutes while you prepare the vegetables.
- The vegetables must be *very finely sliced* as they are only going to cook for 5 minutes. The mangetout can be sliced lengthways if they are big ones, to ensure quicker cooking.
- When the tofu strips have marinaded for 30 minutes the dish is ready to cook. Heat the oil in a wok or large saucepan until almost smoking.
- Tip in the garlic, ginger, bamboo shoots, mangetout, onions, pepper, carrots and mushrooms and toss in the hot oil for 3 minutes, turning frequently.
- Add the beansprouts and toss for a further 1 minute.
- Add the tofu strips, remaining soy sauce and rice, stir in and cover for another minute to heat through.
- Give the mixture a final toss and serve immediately with more soy sauce if liked.
- Not suitable for freezing.

## Stir-fry Vegetables with Rice and Almonds

Another quick to cook, crunchy stir-fry dish packed with nutrients. Makes an attractive, colourful dinner party dish.

8 oz (225 g) brown rice
1 tablespoonful soya, sesame or olive oil

1 green pepper, *thinly* sliced
1 onion, *thinly* sliced
1 small head of fennel, *thinly* sliced
2 courgettes, cut into *thin* 'matchsticks'
2 sticks celery, cut into *thin* strips
2 carrots, cut into *thin* 'matchsticks'
4 oz (100 g) mushrooms, sliced
4 oz (100 g) cauliflower florets, cut into small pieces
8 oz (225 g) fresh or tinned (unsweetened) pineapple, cubed
2 cloves garlic, crushed
Knob fresh ginger, peeled and grated
4 oz (100 g) whole almonds
Pepper
4 tablespoonsful soy sauce.

## Method

- Cook the rice. Drain and rinse to separate the grains.
- Meanwhile prepare the vegetables making sure they are *very finely sliced* as they are only going to cook for 5 minutes.
- Heat the oil in a wok or large saucepan until almost smoking.
- Tip in the pepper, onion, fennel, courgettes, celery, carrots, mushrooms, cauliflower, pineapple, garlic and ginger. Toss in the hot oil for 3 minutes, turning frequently.
- Add the rice, almonds, pepper and soy sauce and toss well to mix. Cover and allow to 'sweat' in the juices for 2 minutes.
- Give a final toss and serve immediately with more soy sauce if liked.
- Not suitable for freezing.

## Vegetable and Chick Pea Couscous

This is my adaptation of a traditional and very popular Middle Eastern dish. The combination of chickpeas, vegetables and mild aromatic spices is an excellent way to make couscous tasty.

8 oz (225 g) couscous
1 stock cube

6 oz (175 g) chickpeas
1 tablespoon olive oil
1 onion, chopped
1 head fennel, chopped
1 red pepper, sliced
8 oz (225 g) mushrooms, sliced
4 courgettes, chopped
2 cloves garlic, crushed
3 oz (75 g) raisins
2 teaspoons ground cardamom
2 teaspoons cumin
2 teaspoons coriander
2 tablespoons fresh chopped parsley
1 teaspoon ground mace
1 tablespoon soy sauce
2 oz (50 g) margarine
Pepper

## *Method*

Set the oven to Gas 4/180°C/350°F.
Grease a 4 pint (2 litre) ovenproof dish.

• Presoak and cook the chick peas. Drain and reserve liquid.
• Make the chick pea liquid up to 1 pint (500 ml), add the stock cube and warm on a low heat until the stock cube has dissolved.
• Put the couscous into a large bowl and pour the warm stock over it. Leave to swell for 10 minutes until all the stock has been absorbed.
• Fry the onion, fennel, pepper, mushrooms, courgettes and garlic in the oil until softening.
• Add the fried vegetables to the soaked couscous with the chick peas, raisins, cardamom, cumin, coriander, parsley, mace, soy sauce and pepper. Mix thoroughly.
• Pile into the prepared dish and dot the margarine over the top in small flakes. Cover with foil and bake for 45 minutes.
• Serve immediately with salads or steamed vegetables.
• Not suitable for freezing.

## Fruity Cashew Nut Pilaff

Don't let the long list of ingredients put you off — this delicious fruity rice dish in very easy to make and has a slightly sweet and sour flavour.

1 onion, chopped
2 cloves garlic, crushed
½ lb (225 g) carrots, chopped
8 oz (225 g) tinned bamboo shoots, sliced
4 oz (100 g) mushrooms, sliced
4 oz (100 g) mangetout, chopped
2 sticks celery, chopped
1 tablespoon oil
4 oz (100 g) dried apricots chopped
2 oz (50 g) raisins
½ pint (275 ml) orange juice
1 medium tin tomatoes, chopped
½ pint (275 ml) stock
1 tablespoon tomato purée
2 tablespoons soy sauce
2 teaspoons coriander
1 teaspoon mace
1 teaspoon ground cardamom
12 oz (350 g) long grain brown rice, washed thoroughly
6 oz (175 g) cashew nuts
2 tablespoons fresh chopped parsley
Pepper

### *Method*

• Fry the onion, garlic, carrots, bamboo shoots, mushrooms, mangetout and celery in the oil until softening.
• Add the apricots, raisins, orange juice, tomatoes, stock, tomato puree, soy sauce, spices, pepper and rice. Stir well, bring to the boil then cover and simmer on a low heat for 45 minutes until the rice is cooked and most of the liquid is absorbed.
• Stir in the cashew nuts and parsley, adjust the seasoning and simmer for another 10 minutes uncovered to absorb the rest of the liquid.

- Serve with a side salad or serve alone for a filling, nutritious meal.
- Freezes well in plastic boxes but use within 6 weeks.


## Vegetable and Tofu Pilaff

This lightly spiced pilaff is quick and easy to make and a tasty way of using tofu. Cooked beans or cashew nuts could be substituted for the tofu if it is not available.

> 12 oz (350 g) long-grain brown rice, washed
> 1 tablespoon oil
> 1 onion, chopped
> 2 cloves garlic, crushed
> 1 green pepper, sliced
> 4 oz (100 g) mangetouts, sliced
> 4 oz (100 g) tinned or frozen sweetcorn
> 4 courgettes, sliced
> 4 oz (100 g) mushrooms, sliced
> Knob fresh ginger, peeled and grated
> 2 oz (50 g) raisins or sultanas
> 2 tablespoons tomato purée
> 2 teaspoons curry powder
> 2 teaspoons coriander
> 2 teaspoons wholegrain mustard
> $\frac{3}{4}$ pint (450 ml) stock
> 8 oz (225 g) *firm* tofu, drained and cubed
> Pepper


*Method*

- Cook the rice. Drain and rinse to separate grains.
- Fry the onion, garlic, pepper, mangetouts, corn, courgettes, mushrooms and ginger in the oil until softening.
- Add the raisins, tomato purée, curry powder, coriander, mustard, stock and pepper. Bring to the boil, cover and simmer on a low heat for 20 minutes. Stir occasionally.
- Add the tofu and simmer for another 5 minutes. Add the rice and simmer for about 5–10 minutes until all the liquid is absorbed. Stir regularly to prevent sticking.
- Serve immediately with a green salad.

• Will freeze in plastic containers but the tofu goes slightly chewy. Use within 8 weeks.

## Sweet and Sour Vegetables with Tofu

Sweet and sour sauce is very popular and this nutritious version using tofu is very quick and easy to make. Serve with rice, couscous, bulgar or millet for a complete meal.

2 onions, thinly sliced
1 red pepper, sliced
2 cloves garlic, crushed
8 oz (225 g) fresh or tinned (unsweetened) pineapple, cubed
4 carrots, cut into *thin* 'matchsticks'
4 courgettes, cut into *thin* 'matchsticks'
4 oz (100 g) mushrooms, sliced
Knob fresh ginger, peeled and grated
2 tablespoons oil
1 medium tin tomatoes, liquidized
½ pint (275 ml) stock
3 tablespoons cider vinegar
4 tablespoons soy sauce
1 tablespoon sugar
1 tablespoon tomato purée
4 oz (100 g) mung bean sprouts
12 oz (350 g) *firm* tofu, cut into small cubes
Pepper
4 heaped teaspoons cornflour

*Method*

• Fry the onion, pepper, garlic, pineapple, carrots, courgettes, mushrooms and ginger in the oil for a few minutes until softening. Cover and leave to 'sweat' for 5 minutes.
• Add the tinned tomatoes, stock, vinegar, soy sauce, sugar and tomato puree. Season well with pepper. Bring to the boil, cover and simmer on a low heat for 10 minutes until the vegetables are soft.
• Add the beansprouts and tofu and simmer for a further 5 minutes.
• Mix the cornflour to a paste with one tablespoon cold

water and add to the sauce, stirring. Stir until thickened and serve immediately with cooked grain of your choice allowing 3 oz (75 g) dry weight per person.

• This recipe can be frozen but the tofu will go slightly chewy. If making specifically for the freezer, leave the tofu out and add after thawing the sauce. Use within 6 weeks.


## Vegetable Stroganoff

This is a rich, tasty dish made nice and creamy by the addition of silken tofu. A good dinner party dish for impressing non-vegan friends! Quick and easy to make.

2 tablespoons olive oil
1 onion, chopped
2 cloves garlic, crushed
4 oz (100 g) mushrooms, sliced
2 sticks celery, chopped
4 courgettes, sliced
2 tablespoons flour
1 pint (500 ml) strong stock
2 teaspoons tarragon
2 tablespoons fresh chopped parsley
8 oz (225 g) *silken* tofu
2 teaspoons miso
Pepper


*Method*

• Fry the onion, garlic, mushrooms, pepper, celery and courgettes in the oil until softening. Cover and 'sweat' for 5 minutes.
• Stir in the flour and cook for one minute.
• *Remove from heat* and stir in the stock gradually to avoid lumps. Add the tarragon, parsley and pepper.
• Return to a low heat and stir until the sauce has thickened.
• Put the tofu in a liquidizer with the miso and 2 tablespoons water. Whizz until smooth and creamy.
• Add the tofu cream to the sauce and stir in. Bring to serving temperature but *do not boil* or the beneficial enzymes in the miso will be destroyed.

- Serve with cooked grain or pasta of your choice (allowing 3 oz (75 g) dry weight per person) and a salad.
- To freeze — leave the tofu cream out of the recipe. Freeze the sauce in a plastic container, thaw and reheat gently in a pan. Add the tofu cream and serve as normal.

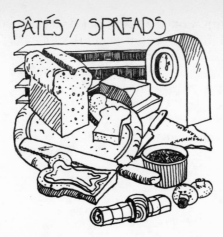

# PÂTÉS / SPREADS

### Lentil and Walnut Pâté

This delicious pâté tastes and looks remarkably 'meaty'. A good one to try on non-vegans.

2 oz (50 g) red lentils, thoroughly washed
2 oz (50 g) ground walnuts
1 onion, grated
1 clove garlic, crushed
1 teaspoon thyme
1 teaspoon yeast extract/miso
Black pepper
Knob margarine
Parsley to garnish

### Method

• Fry the onion and garlic in the margarine for a few minutes.
• Add the lentils and enough water to just cover them. Bring to the boil and skim off any froth.
• Add the yeast extract, thyme and pepper and simmer for 15 minutes until the lentils are soft and have absorbed the water (more water may need to be added during cooking but do not make it too sloppy).
• If miso is used rather than yeast extract add it at the end of cooking time so it is not boiled or the enzyme it contains will be destroyed.
• Cool the lentil mixture slightly then stir in the walnuts.
• Pour into a bowl or individual ramekins and chill. Garnish with parsley.

- Serve with toast, crackers or biscuits.
- Keeps 3–4 days in fridge and freezes well. Use within 6 weeks if frozen.

## Smoked Tofu and Aubergine Pâté

The smoked tofu gives this nutritious pâté a unique flavour that makes it ideal as a luxurious dinner party starter.

    1 large aubergine
    6 oz (175 g) smoked *firm* tofu, drained and mashed
    1 onion, finely chopped
    2 cloves garlic, crushed
    1 tablespoonful olive oil
    Rind and juice ½ lemon
    1 tablespoon tahini
    2 teaspoons tomato purée
    Black pepper

### *Method*

Set oven to Gas 6/200°C/400°F.

- Top and tail the aubergine, wrap it in foil and bake for 30 minutes until soft. Cool slightly.
- Peel the aubergine and chop it roughly. Put in a blender or liquidizer with the tofu, lemon juice and rind, tahini and tomato purée.
- Fry the onion and garlic in the oil until browning. Add to the ingredients in the blender, season well with pepper and whizz on a high speed until smooth and creamy.
- Pour into 4 individual ramekin dishes or a bowl and chill for 2 hours before serving. Garnish with parsley and lemon twists and serve with toast or crackers to achieve protein complementarity. May also be used as a sandwich spread. Keeps 2–3 days in the fridge.
- Not suitable for freezing.

## Lemon and Herb Bean Pâté

A smooth herby pâté with a delicious tang of lemon. Nice as a starter with toast or as a sandwich spread.

4 oz (100 g) haricot beans
1 small onion, finely chopped
1 clove garlic, crushed
1 stick celery, chopped
1 tablespoon oil
1 tablespoon fresh chopped parsley
1 teaspoon tarragon
1 teaspoon thyme
1 dessertspoon tomato purée
1 teaspoon yeast extract
Rind 1 small lemon
Pepper

## Method

- Presoak and cook the beans. Drain and reserve liquid.
- Fry the onion, garlic and celery in the oil until softening.
- Liquidize or mash the beans to a smooth purée with the fried vegetables, parsley, tarragon, thyme, tomato puree, yeast extract, lemon rind and pepper. Add 1–2 tablespoons reserved bean liquid to moisten if necessary.
- Pour into a bowl or individual ramekins and chill before serving. Garnish with lemon twists and serve with bread or crackers made from grain to achieve protein complementarity.
- Keeps 4 days in the fridge and freezes well. Use within 6 weeks if frozen.

## Green Pea and Sunflower Seed Pâté

A rich tasty pâté with the distinctive flavour of roasted sunflower seeds. Good as a starter with toast.

4 oz (100 g) green split peas, washed thoroughly
1 stock cube
1 teaspoon tarragon
2 bayleaves
2 oz (50 g) sunflower seeds
1 onion, finely chopped
2 cloves garlic, crushed
1 tablespoon oil
1 tablespoon fresh chopped parsley
Pepper

*Method*

Set oven to Gas 5/190°C/375°F.

• Put the split peas in a pan with the stock cube, tarragon and bayleaves. Cover with water, bring to the boil then simmer, covered, on a low heat for 40 minutes until the peas can be beaten to a smooth purée. (Add more water during cooking as necessary and stir regularly to prevent sticking). Remove bayleaves.
• Spread the sunflower seeds on a baking tray and roast them in the oven for 5 minutes until golden brown. Allow to cool, then grind in a liquidizer to a fine powder.
• Fry the onion and garlic in the oil until softening. Stir into the cooked pea puree with the ground seeds, parsley and pepper.
• Pile into a bowl or individual ramekins and garnish with parsley and lemon slices. Chill before serving.
• Keeps 3–4 days in the fridge and freezes well. Use within 6 weeks.


**Tofu and Tahini Spread**

This creamy, nutritious spread has an attractive pale green colour due to the fresh parsley and is ideal as a sandwich spread. Very quick and easy to make.

8 oz (225 g) *firm* tofu, drained
1 small onion, finely chopped
2 cloves garlic, crushed
1 tablespoon olive oil
2 tablespoons tahini
2 teaspoons miso
2 tablespoons fresh chopped parsley
1 teaspoon nutmeg
Pepper


*Method*

• Fry the onion and garlic in the oil until softening.
• Put the fried vegetables into a liquidizer with all the other ingredients and whizz until smooth and thick.
• Pour into a bowl or ramekins and chill until firm. Garnish

with tomato or red pepper rings for a contrast in colour and serve with grain bread or crackers to improve the protein value.
• Keeps 3–4 days in the fridge. Not suitable for freezing.


## Hummus

A delicious, garlicy chick pea dip from the Middle East. Hummus should be smooth, creamy and runny, not thick and pasty like so many commercially made varieties.

8 oz (225 g) chick peas
2 cloves garlic crushed
4 tablespoons olive oil
Juice 2 lemons
1 tablespoon tahini (sesame seed paste)
Black pepper
Paprika or chopped parsley to serve


### *Method*

• Presoak and cook the chick peas. Drain and reserve the liquid.
• Put the chickpeas, garlic, oil, lemon juice, tahini and 6 tablespoons of the chickpea liquid in a blender. Whizz on a high speed until the hummus is white and creamy. Season generously with pepper.
• If a runnier texture is required for dips add more cooking water, if a thicker texture is required for sandwiches, add less liquid.
• Pour the hummus into a bowl or individual ramekins and garnish with paprika and/or parsley.
• Serve with crudités of cucumber, cauliflower, carrot, pepper etc. or as a spread on crackers or bread.
• Keeps 4–5 days in the fridge and freezes well. If frozen, use within 6 weeks or the garlic flavour will intensify.
• If you don't like raw garlic, the garlic can be crushed and added to the chickpeas during cooking so you will still have the flavour.

## Spicy Red Bean Pâté

This lightly spiced pâté is very easy to make and equally nice as a starter or in sandwiches.

4 oz (100 g) red kidney beans
1 onion, chopped
2 cloves garlic, crushed
Knob fresh ginger, grated
½ green pepper, sliced
1 stick celery, chopped
1 tablespoon oil
2 teaspoons tomato purée
1 teaspoon wholegrain mustard
1 teaspoon coriander
1 teaspoon cumin
2 teaspoons pickle
Pepper

### Method

- Presoak and cook the beans. Drain and reserve liquid.
- Fry the onion, garlic, ginger, pepper and celery in the oil until softening.
- Put the fried vegetables and the cooked beans in a liquidizer or blender with 2 tablespoons of the bean liquid and all the other ingredients.
- Whizz until smooth. Chill before serving with crackers, bread, toast etc.
- Keeps 3–4 days in the fridge and freezes well but use within 6 weeks because of the spices.

*Note:* The pâté must be served with grain bread or crackers in order to achieve protein complementarity.

## Chick Pea and Vegetable Pâté

A tasty pâté with a smooth texture suitable for sandwiches or toast.

4 oz (100 g) chick peas
2 carrots, grated
2 cloves garlic, crushed
1 onion, chopped

1 stick celery, chopped
½ green pepper, chopped
2 oz (50 g) mushrooms, sliced
1 tablespoon oil
1 tablespoon soy sauce
1 teaspoon nutmeg
1 teaspoon coriander
2 teaspoons tomato purée
1 tablespoon fresh chopped parsley
Pepper

*Method*

- Presoak and cook the chickpeas. Drain and reserve liquid.
- Fry the carrot, garlic, onion, celery, pepper and mushrooms in the oil for a few minutes until softening.
- Put the vegetables, cooked chickpeas and all the other ingredients in a blender or liquidizer with 3 tablespoons chick pea water.
- Whizz until smooth and chill before serving.
- Keeps 3–4 days in the fridge and freezes well.
- Serve with bread or crackers made from grain to achieve good protein complementarity.

## Brown Lentil and Apple Spread

An unusual combination of flavours and textures makes this a tasty sandwich filling.

4 oz (100 g) brown lentils, washed thoroughly
1 stock cube
½ teaspoon sage
1 bay leaf
1 tablespoon olive oil
1 onion, chopped finely
2 cloves garlic, crushed
1 medium cooking apple, peeled, cored and grated
1 teaspoon mace
Pepper

*Method*

- Put the lentils in a pan with the stock cube, sage and

235

bayleaf. Cover with water and bring to the boil. Skim off any froth and then simmer, covered for 30 minutes until the lentils are soft and can be mashed roughly. (Add more water during cooking as necessary but do not make too wet).

• Fry the onion, garlic and apple in the oil until soft. Add to the lentils with the mace and pepper. Stir well and remove the bay leaf.

• Chill for 2 hours before serving. Serve with bread or crackers to achieve good protein complementarity.

• Keeps 3–4 days in the fridge and freezes well. Use within 6 weeks.


### Yellow Pea and Mushroom Pâté

Delicious in sandwiches or on crackers, this tasty pâté is very popular with children.

> 4 oz (100 g) yellow split peas, washed thoroughly
> 1 stock cube
> 1 bay leaf
> 1 teaspoon savory
> 4 oz (100 g) mushrooms, finely chopped
> 1 onion, finely chopped
> 1 clove garlic, crushed
> Knob margarine
> 1 tablespoon fresh chopped parsley
> 1 teaspoon coriander
> $\frac{1}{2}$ teaspoon yeast extract
> Rind 1 lemon
> Pepper

### *Method*

• Put the split peas, stock cube, bayleaf and savory in a pan. Cover with water, bring to the boil then cover and simmer on a low heat for 40 minutes until the peas can be beaten to a smooth purée. (Add more water during cooking as necessary and stir regularly to prevent sticking).

• Fry the mushrooms, onion and garlic in the margarine until softening. Add to the pea purée with all the other ingredients. Season well and mix thoroughly.

• Press into 4 ramekins and chill before serving. Keeps 3–4 days in the fridge.

- Freezes well but use within 6 weeks.
- In order for complementarity to be achieved the pâté should be served with bread or crackers made from grain.

## Hazelnut and Tofu Spread

A quick, easy and very nutritious spread. Popular as a starter with toast or in sandwiches. *This recipe is dedicated to Debbie.*

    4 oz (100 g) *firm* tofu, drained and mashed
    2 oz (50 g) ground hazelnuts
    1 small onion, grated
    1 carrot, grated
    1 clove garlic, crushed
    2 oz (50 g) mushrooms, finely chopped
    1 tablespoon olive oil
    1 tablespoon fresh chopped parsley
    1 tablespoon soy sauce
    2 teaspoons tomato purée
    1 teaspoon coriander
    Black pepper

### *Method*

- Fry the onion, carrot, garlic and mushrooms in the oil until soft.
- Combine with all the other ingredients and mix thoroughly.
- Chill before serving.
- Keeps 3–4 days in the fridge but is not particularly good frozen as the tofu goes 'chewy'.

## Brazil Nut and Vegetable Spread

A smooth, tasty spread which can be used on crackers or as a dip with raw vegetables.

    4 oz (100 g) brazil nuts, ground finely
    Knob margarine
    1 onion, chopped
    2 cloves garlic, crushed
    4 oz (100 g) mushrooms, sliced

½ red pepper, sliced
2 sticks celery, chopped
1 small or ½ large aubergine
2 tablespoons fresh chopped parsley
2 teaspoons miso
Pepper

### Method

Set oven to Gas 6/200°C/400°F.

• Top and tail the aubergine, wrap it in foil and bake for 30 minutes until soft. Cool slightly then peel and chop roughly.
• Fry the onion, garlic, mushrooms, pepper and celery in the margarine until softening.
• Put the fried vegetables, cooked aubergine and brazil nuts in a liquidizer with the parsley, miso and pepper. Whizz until smooth.
• Pour into a bowl and chill before serving. Serve with grain bread or crackers to achieve protein complementarity.
• Keeps 3–4 days in the fridge and freezes well but use within 6 weeks.

SAVOURY SAUCES

## Tomato and Garlic Sauce

Probably the most popular sauce of all, this one goes well with virtually anything! Doubles up as a casserole base or binder for pie fillings. (To serve 4.)

1 clove garlic, crushed
1 oz (25 g) margarine
1 tablespoon flour
½ pint (275 ml) stock
2 tablespoons tomato purée
1 teaspoon basil
1 tablespoon fresh chopped parsley
Black pepper

### *Method*

• Melt margarine and sauté the garlic gently for 1 minute taking care not to let it brown.
• Stir in the flour and cook on a *low* heat for another minute.
• *Remove from heat* and add the stock gradually, stirring vigorously to avoid lumps.
• Add tomato purée, basil and parsley. Season well with pepper.
• Return to the heat and bring to the boil, stirring. Allow to simmer on a low heat for 1–2 minutes until sauce is thick.
• Serve with burgers, roasts, bakes etc. The flavour is even better if allowed to stand for 30 minutes before serving so the garlic flavour develops.

- Can be frozen but use within 6 weeks.

## Mustard, Garlic and Tarragon Sauce

A delicious combination of flavours, this rich sauce adds a spicy, but not hot, flavour to any dish. (To serve 4.)

    1 clove garlic, crushed
    1 oz (25 g) margarine
    1 tablespoon flour
    ¼ pint (150 ml) soya milk
    ¼ pint (150 ml) stock
    1 teaspoon tarragon
    2 teaspoons wholegrain mustard
    ½ teaspoon yeast extract
    Pepper

### *Method*

- Melt margarine and sauté garlic gently for 1 minute taking care not to allow it to brown.
- Stir in the flour and cook for another minute on a *low* heat.
- *Remove from the heat* and add the milk and stock gradually, stirring vigorously to avoid lumps.
- Add tarragon, mustard and yeast extract. Season well with pepper.
- Return to the heat and bring to the boil stirring. Allow to simmer on a low heat for 1–2 minutes until sauce is thick.
- Serve with burgers and roasts. The flavour improves if allowed to stand for 30 minutes before serving.
- Can be frozen but use within 6 weeks.

## Miso Gravy

A nice, rich sauce suitable for serving with roasts. Miso gives a very savoury flavour but yeast extract can be used if preferred. (Serves 4.)

    1 oz (25 g) margarine
    1 small onion, finely chopped
    1 clove garlic, crushed
    1 tablespoon flour

$\frac{1}{2}$ pint (275 ml) stock
1 heaped teaspoon miso
$\frac{1}{2}$ teaspoon yeast extract
Pepper

## *Method*

- Fry the onion and garlic in the margarine until soft.
- Add the flour and cook for one minute over a *low* heat.
- *Remove from heat* and add the stock gradually stirring vigorously to avoid lumps.
- Add the yeast extract and pepper and return to heat. Bring to the boil and simmer until it has thickened, stirring.
- Pour the gravy into a liquidizer and add the miso. Blend until smooth and miso is mixed in.
- Reheat gently to serving temperature but *do not boil* or the enzymes in the miso will be destroyed.
- Alternatively, if a textured sauce is preferred, dissolve the miso in a tablespoon of warm water and add to the thickened sauce. Stir in and serve without liquidizing.
- Freezes well but use within 6 weeks.

## Sherry Sauce

A rich sauce suitable for special occasions. Serve with nut roast or burgers for a luxurious touch. (To serve 4.)

1 oz (25 g) margarine
1 oz (25 g) flour
1 small onion, finely chopped
1 clove garlic, crushed
8 fl oz (225 ml) stock
2 fl oz (50 ml dry sherry
1 teaspoon yeast extract
Pepper

## *Method*

- Fry the onion and garlic in the margarine until softening.
- Stir in the flour and fry for one minute.
- *Remove from heat* and add the stock gradually stirring continuously to avoid lumps. Stir in the sherry, yeast extract and pepper.

- Return to a low heat and stir until thickened.
- Freeze in plastic containers and use within 6 weeks.


## Peanut Sauce (Indonesian-Style)

A lovely rich creamy sauce with an authentic Indonesian flavour. Ideal as a sauce for cooked vegetables or as a complement to burgers, pancakes and stuffed vegetables. (To serve 4.)

> 1 tablespoon oil
> 1 small onion, finely chopped
> 1 clove garlic, crushed
> ½ pint (275 ml) stock
> 2 tablespoons peanut butter
> ¼ teaspoon tabasco sauce
> 1 teaspoon maple syrup or sugar
> 1 teaspoon miso
> 1 oz (25 g) solid coconut cream (e.g. Sharwoods)
> Pepper

*Method*

- Fry the onion and garlic in the oil until softening.
- Add the stock, peanut butter, tabasco, maple syrup and pepper. Bring to the boil, cover and simmer on a low heat for 10 minutes. Cool slightly.
- Pour into a liquidizer and whizz until smooth and creamy. Return to pan.
- Add the miso and coconut cream (cut into small pieces) and stir over a low heat until blended. Bring to serving temperature but *do not boil* or the beneficial enzymes in the miso will be destroyed.
- Freeze in plastic containers and use within 6 weeks.


## Lemon and Coriander Seed Sauce

An aromatic sauce that goes well with stuffed vegetables, pancakes or burgers. (To serve 4.)

> 1 oz (25 g) margarine
> 1 oz (25 g) flour
> ½ pint (275 ml) soya milk

Rind $\frac{1}{2}$ lemon
1 teaspoon miso
3 teaspoons coriander seeds
Pepper

## Method

• Crush the coriander seeds to a fine powder in a pestle and mortar or in a bowl with a rolling pin.
• Put the margarine, flour, soya milk, lemon rind and crushed coriander into a pan and whisk with a balloon whisk, over a low heat until the margarine has melted.
• Bring to the boil, whisking continuously until the sauce has thickened and is bubbling.
• *Remove from heat* and whisk in the miso and pepper. Serve immediately.
• If the sauce has to be made in advance reheat gently to serving temperature but *do not boil* or the beneficial enzymes in the miso will be destroyed.
• Freeze in plastic containers and use within 6 weeks.

## Parsley and Tarragon Sauce

A variation on the traditional parsley sauce that goes well with any burgers, roasts or pancakes. (To serve 4).

1 oz (25 g) flour
1 oz (25 g) margarine
$\frac{1}{2}$ pint (275 ml) soya milk
2 tablespoons fresh chopped parsley
2 teaspoons tarragon
Pepper
1 teaspoon miso

## Method

• Put the flour, margarine, soya milk, parsley and tarragon in a pan. Whisk with a balloon whisk over a low heat until the margarine melts.
• Bring to the boil whisking continuously until the sauce thickens and is bubbling.
• *Remove from the heat* and whisk in the miso and pepper. Serve immediately.

- If the sauce is made in advance, reheat gently but *do not boil* or the beneficial enzymes in the miso will be destroyed.
- The sauce freezes well in plastic containers but use within 6 weeks.


## Barbecue Sauce

Delicious with all burgers and roasts, this sauce can also be used as a spicy base for casseroles and curries. (To serve 4.)

> 1 onion, finely chopped
> 2 cloves garlic, crushed
> 1 small piece fresh ginger, peeled and grated
> 1 tablespoon oil
> Medium tin tomatoes, chopped/liquidized
> Rind and juice 1 small lemon
> 3 dessertspoons brown sauce
> 1 dessertspoon soy sauce
> 1 dessertspoon cider vinegar
> 2 tablespoons molasses sugar
> Black pepper


### *Method*

- Fry the onion, garlic and ginger in the oil until softening.
- Add all the other ingredients and season well with pepper.
- Bring to the boil, stirring, then lower heat, cover and simmer for 15–20 minutes until thick and liquid is well reduced. Stir occasionally.
- The sauce may be served as it is or liquidized for a smoother texture and then reheated.
- Can be frozen but use within 6 weeks.


## Onion Sauce

A thick sauce that is nice for a change with pies, roasts or burgers. (To serve 4.)

> 1 oz (25 g) margarine
> 2 onions, finely chopped
> 1 clove garlic, crushed

1 oz (25 g) flour
¼ pint (150 ml) strong stock
¼ pint (150 ml) soya milk
1 teaspoon wholegrain mustard
Pepper

## Method

• Fry the onion and garlic in the margarine until browning.
• Stir in the flour and cook for one minute.
• Remove from heat and add the stock and soya milk gradually, stirring continuously to avoid lumps. Add the mustard and pepper.
• Return to a low heat and stir until thickened and bubbling.
• The sauce freezes well in plastic containers but use within 6 weeks.

## Mushroom and Sherry Sauce

A luxurious version of the basic mushroom sauce that is delicious with special meals such as nutroast. (To serve 4).

1 oz (25 g) margarine
1 clove garlic, crushed
4 oz (100 g) mushrooms, finely chopped
1 oz (25 g) flour
¼ pint (150 ml) stock
¼ pint (150 ml) soya milk
1½ tablespoons dry sherry
Pepper

## Method

• Fry the garlic and mushrooms in the margarine until softening.
• Stir in the flour and cook for one minute.
• *Remove from heat* and add the stock, milk and sherry gradually, stirring continuously to avoid lumps. Season well with pepper.
• Return to a low heat and stir until thickened and bubbling.
• Freeze in plastic containers and use within 6 weeks.

## Curry Sauce

This delicious thick sauce is very mild and sweet making it ideal for spicing up burgers or roasts. It can also be used as a base for a curry if vegetables, nuts, tofu or beans are added. (To serve 4.)

1 small onion, finely chopped
1 clove garlic, crushed
1 stick celery, chopped
1 small cooking apple, peeled, cored and chopped
1 tablespoon oil
1 small tin tomatoes, liquidized or chopped
1 tablespoon tomato purée
½ pint (275 ml) stock
1 teaspoon curry powder
2 teaspoons cumin
2 teaspoons coriander
1 teaspoon cardamom
1 teaspoon wholegrain mustard
1 teaspoon pickle
1 teaspoon garam masala
Pepper

### Method

• Fry the onion, garlic, celery and apple in the oil for a few minutes until softening.
• Add the curry powder, cumin, coriander, cardamom, mustard and pickle and fry for a further minute, stirring continuously.
• Add the tinned tomatoes, tomato purée, stock and pepper and bring to the boil. Cover and simmer on a low heat for 30 minutes stirring occasionally.
• Add the garam masala and heat through on a low heat.
• Allow the sauce to stand for 30 minutes prior to serving to allow the full flavour to develop. Reheat gently and serve.
• Can be frozen but use within 6 weeks.

## Mushroom, Tomato and Ginger Sauce

This rich sauce has the lovely subtle flavour of fresh ginger. It is ideal for serving with any roasts, burgers or pancakes. (To serve 4.)

1 oz (25 g) margarine
1 onion, *very finely* chopped
1 clove garlic, crushed
Knob fresh ginger, peeled and grated
4 oz (100 g) mushrooms, *very finely* chopped
1 heaped tablespoon flour
½ pint (275 ml) stock
2 tablespoons tomato purée
1 teaspoon miso
Pepper

## Method

• Fry the onion, garlic, ginger and mushrooms in the margarine until soft.
• Add the flour and cook for one minute.
• *Remove from heat* and add the stock gradually, stirring continuously to avoid lumps. Add the tomato purée and pepper.
• Return to a low heat and stir until thick.
• Stir in the miso (*but do not boil* or the beneficial enzymes it contains will be destroyed), and serve immediately.
• Freeze in plastic containers and use within 6 weeks.

## Sweet and Sour Sauce

Very popular with burgers and bakes, this sauce is also excellent as a base for sweet and sour vegetables or stir-fried dishes. (To serve 4.)

1 onion, finely chopped
½ green pepper, finely chopped
1 clove garlic, crushed
4 oz (100 g) fresh or tinned pineapple, chopped
1 tablespoon oil
Small tin tomatoes, liquidized or chopped
1½ tablespoons cider vinegar
2 tablespoons soy sauce
1 dessertspoon molasses sugar

1 dessertspoon tomato purée
¼ pint (150 ml) stock
Pepper
2 level teaspoons cornflour

### Method

- Fry the pepper, onion, garlic and pineapple in the oil for a few minutes until softening.
- Add the tomatoes, vinegar, soy sauce, sugar, tomato purée, stock and pepper. Bring to the boil then cover, reduce the heat, and simmer for 10 minutes.
- Mix the cornflour with 1 tablespoon cold water to form a paste. Stir into the sauce. Simmer until the sauce has thickened.
- The sweetness or sourness of the sauce can be adjusted to personal taste by adding more or less sugar and vinegar respectively.
- Can be frozen but use within 6 weeks.

### Tahini and Miso Sauce

This deliciously rich sauce makes a very nutritious accompaniment to savoury pancakes, burgers or roasts. (To serve 4.)

1 oz (25 g) margarine
1 oz (25 g) flour
½ pint (275 ml) soya milk
2 teaspoons miso
1 dessertspoon tahini
1 teaspoon coriander
Pepper

### Method

- Put the margarine, flour and milk in a pan and whisk with a balloon whisk over a low heat until the margarine has melted.
- Bring to the boil, whisking continuously until the sauce has thickened and is bubbling.
- *Remove from heat* and whisk in the miso, tahini, coriander and pepper. Stir until smooth and serve immediately.

•   If the sauce has to be made in advance reheat gently to serving temperature but *do not boil* or the beneficial enzymes in the miso will be destroyed.

•   The sauce freezes successfully in plastic containers but use within 6 weeks.

## Fruit Pie

A traditional favourite, made wholefood. Any fruits in season can be used but some particularly nice combinations are:
Blackberry and apple: 3 cooking apples with about 8 oz (225 g) blackberries
Spiced apple and pear: 2 cooking apples, 2 pears, 1 tablespoon sultanas, 2 teaspoons mixed spice, rind of one orange
Apricot and raspberry: 1 lb (450 g) apricots with about 8 oz (225 g) raspberries

> 6 oz (175 g) shortcrust pastry or nut pastry.
> (6 oz/175 g flour, 3 oz/75 g margarine – see recipe p. 138).
> Fruit of your choice
> Soya milk to glaze

### Method

Set oven to Gas 6/200°C/400°F.

- Make the pastry. Roll out two-thirds of it to fit an 8″ (20 cm) pie dish or flan ring.
- Chop the chosen fruit finely and fill the case. (Note: the peel can be left on or taken off fruit, according to preference. I always use raw fruit (except rhubarb) as it holds its shape better when cooked. I never add liquid as it makes the pastry soggy and I never sweeten fruit unless very 'tart' in which case I sprinkle 1 tablespoon muscavado sugar on top of the fruit).
- Brush the edges of the pastry with soya milk then roll out the remaining pastry to fit the top of the pie.

- Cover the fruit with the pastry and press the edges of pastry together to seal. Trim the edges and flute as required. Make a slit in the top.
- Brush the top of the pie with soya milk and bake for 30 minutes until the pastry is golden.
- Serve hot or cold with nut cream, soya custard, undiluted Plamil etc. (Serves 4–6.)
- Freezes better raw. Cook from frozen.

## Fruit Crumble

Another favourite. Any fruit can be used with this delicious crunchy topping but some nice combinations are listed below.
Rhubarb and orange: 1 lb (450 g) rhubarb with the rind and segments of 2 oranges. Will probably need sweetening.
Pear and ginger: 6–8 pears with a knob of fresh ginger peeled and grated on top of it.
Dried fruit: about 12 oz (350 g) dried fruit e.g. apricots, prunes, dates, peaches etc. stewed in apple or orange juice until soft.

Fruit of your choice
2 tablespoons orange or apple juice
6 oz (175 g) flour
3 oz (75 g) margarine
1 tablespoon ground hazels or almonds
1 tablespoon rolled oats
1 tablespoon molasses sugar

*Method*

Set oven to Gas 5/190°C/375°F.

- *Either* put the raw fruit and the orange or apple juice straight into a 2 pint (1 litre) ovenproof dish *or* stew it gently in the juice for 5 minutes to soften it and then put into the dish. (The second method is better for harder fruits such as rhubarb and apples and the first method is better for soft fruits such as pears, raspberries, blackcurrants etc.)
- Sweeten the fruit if necessary with 1 tablespoon molasses sugar — most fruits are better unsweetened.
- Rub the margarine into the flour until the mixture resembles breadcrumbs then stir in the nuts, oats, seeds and sugar.
- Sprinkle the crumble mixture on top of the fruit loosely. Do not flatten down.

- Bake for 20–30 minutes until the crumble is well browned.
- Serve with soya custard, nutcream, etc.
- Freezes better raw. Cook from frozen.

*Variation:* Try mixing 1 teaspoon ground coriander, nutmeg or mixed spice into the crumble topping for an interesting difference in flavour.

### Apple and Sultana Charlotte

This gorgeous pudding is much lighter than it looks and sounds and is especially nice at Christmas as a change from rich Christmas pudding.

6 oz (175 g) wholemeal breadcrumbs
3 oz (75 g) ground hazelnuts
2 oz (50 g) margarine
Rind 1 small lemon
1½ lb (725 g) cooking apples, peeled, cored and sliced
3 tablespoons orange juice
3 oz (75 g) sultanas
1 teaspoon mixed spice

### *Method*

Set the oven to Gas 4/180°C/350°F.
Grease a 2 pint (1 litre) ovenproof dish.

- Put the apples, sultanas and orange juice in a pan and stew on a low heat for 5 minutes, stirring occasionally, until the apple is softening. Stir in the spice.
- Melt the margarine and stir in the breadcrumbs, hazelnuts and lemon rind. Mix thoroughly.
- Put one third of the crumb mixture on the base of the dish and spread half the apple mixture on top. Cover with another layer of crumbs, then apple and finally a layer of crumbs.
- Bake for 30 minutes until golden brown and crisp. Serve with nutcream, soya custard, tofu cream etc.
- Better frozen raw and cooked from frozen.

### Rhubarb and Apricot Charlotte

A lovely combination of flavours and textures, this tangy sweet is guaranteed to be a family favourite.

1 lb (500 g) young cherry rhubarb, chopped into 1″ (2.5 cm) pieces
4 oz (100 g) dried apricots, roughly chopped
½ teaspoon cinnamon
½ teaspoon nutmeg
2–3 dessertspoons soft brown sugar
6 oz (175 g) wholemeal breadcrumbs
4 oz (100 g) vegan digestive biscuits, crushed (e.g. *Mitchelhills, Doves Farm, McVities Wholemeal, Raskusens*)
4 oz (100 g) margarine
Rind and juice 1 orange

*Method*

Set oven to Gas 4/180°C/350°F.
Grease a 2 pint (1 litre) ovenproof dish.
• Squeeze the juice from the orange and put in a pan with the apricots and ¼ pint (150 ml) water. Bring to the boil, cover, and simmer gently on a low heat for 10 minutes until the apricots are softening. (Add more water if the fruit is going dry).
• Add the rhubarb and simmer for a further 5 minutes until the rhubarb is breaking down. (The mixture should be fairly moist.
• Stir in the spices and enough sugar to sweeten to your taste.
• Melt the margarine and add the breadcrumbs, biscuits and orange rind. Stir well to coat thoroughly.
• Put a third of the breadcrumb mixture on the base of the dish and spread half the rhubarb mixture on top. Cover with another third of breadcrumbs, then the rest of the rhubarb and finally a layer of breadcrumbs.
• Bake for 25–30 minutes until golden brown.
• Serve with nut cream, soya custard etc.
• Better frozen raw and cooked from frozen.

**Hazelnut Eve's Pudding**

A vegan wholefood version of one of granny's favourite recipes.

2 large cooking apples, peeled, cored and sliced
3 oz (75 g) wholemeal flour

2 oz (50 g) ground hazelnuts
3 oz (75 g) molasses sugar
2 fl oz (50 ml) oil
5 fl oz (150 ml) water
2 teaspoons baking powder
1 teaspoon mixed spice

### Method

Set oven to Gas 4/180°C/350°F.
Grease a 2 pint (1 litre) baking dish or deep 7″ (18 cm) cake tin.

• Heat the water, oil and sugar together in a pan until the sugar dissolves. *Do not boil.* Leave to cool.
• Mix the flour, nuts, baking powder and spice together in a bowl. When the sugar liquid is cool add to the bowl and mix thoroughly to form a runny sponge batter.
*Note: the sugar liquid must be cold before it is added or the baking powder will be activated before reaching the oven and the sponge will not rise.*
• Put the apples in the base of the prepared dish and pour the sponge batter over.
• Bake for 30–40 minutes until the sponge is brown and firm and a skewer comes out clean.
• Serve with soya custard or apricot sauce.
• Can be frozen but will need to be served with a sauce or custard as the sponge goes a little bit dry on freezing.
*Variation:*Try using other fruits such as plums, apricots, blackcurrants, raspberries, rhubarb etc.

### Date and Prune Chocolate Sponge

This lovely sweet which has a high iron content is very rich and will probably serve 6 people depending on the type of meal. Definitely not one to serve after a heavy main course! (Serves 4–6).

4 oz (100 g) dried prunes
4 oz (100 g) dates
½ pint (275 ml) apple juice
4 oz (100 g) wholemeal flour
1 oz (25 g) cocoa or carob powder

254

Rind 1 orange
2 teaspoons baking powder
2 fl oz (50 ml) oil
5 fl oz (150 ml) water
3 oz (75 g) molasses sugar

## Method

Soak the prunes in the apple juice overnight or for at least 6 hours until swollen and plump.
Set oven to Gas 4/180°C/350°F.
Grease a 2 pint (1 litre) ovenproof dish.

• Heat the water, oil and sugar together in a pan until the sugar dissolves. *Do not boil.* Leave to cool.
• Stew the prunes in the apple juice left after soaking for 10 minutes until they are soft. Remove from the juice and de-stone. Chop roughly.
• Add the dates to the remaining apple juice and stew for 5 minutes until soft and plump and all the juice has been absorbed. Mix the dates with the chopped prunes and spread on the base of the prepared dish.
• Sieve the cocoa and baking powder into a bowl and add the flour and orange rind. Stir in the cool sugar liquid to form a thick sponge batter. *Note: The sugar liquid must be cold before it is added or the baking powder will be activated before reaching the oven and the sponge will not rise.*
• Spread the sponge on top of the fruit and bake for 30–40 minutes until the sponge is risen and firm and a skewer comes out clean.
• Serve with soya custard, soya ice cream or orange sauce.
• Can be frozen but the sponge goes a little bit dry. As long as a sauce is served with it though, this is perfectly acceptable.

## Pineapple Upside-Down Pudding

Definitely naughty but nice! A vegan, wholefood version of everyone's favourite.

Base:
  14 oz (400 g) tin unsweetened pineapple pieces
  2 oz (50 g) soft brown sugar
  4 fl oz (100 g) water
  2 oz (50 g) margarine

1 teaspoon cinnamon
4 teaspoons cornflour
Rind and juice 1 lemon
Sponge:
    5 oz (150 g) plain flour
    2 teaspoons baking powder
    1 teaspoon cinnamon
    3 oz (75 g) soft brown sugar
    2 fl oz (50 ml) sunflower oil
    5 fl oz (150 ml) water

*Method*

• Set oven to Gas 4/180°C/350°F.

Grease a deep 7″ (18 cm) cake tin or 2 pint (1 litre) ovenproof dish.

*Make the base first* – mix the cornflour with the juice from the pineapple until dissolved. Put in a pan with the water, sugar, margarine, cinnamon, lemon rind and juice.

• Stir over a low heat until the sugar has dissolved then bring to the boil and simmer to thicken. Put to one side.

• *To make the sponge* – heat the oil, water and sugar together until the sugar has dissolved. *Do not boil.* Leave to cool.

• Mix the flour, baking powder and cinnamon together in a bowl and when the sugar liquid is cool stir it in to form a runny sponge batter. *Note: The sugar liquid must be cold before it is added or the baking powder will be activated before reaching the oven and the sponge will not rise.*

• Put the pineapple cubes on the base of the prepared tin and pour 4 tablespoons of the pineapple sauce over it. Spread the sponge batter on top and bake for 20–25 minutes until the sponge is set and a skewer comes out clean.

• Turn out onto a plate so the pineapple is on top of the pudding. Reheat the remaining sauce and serve with it.

• Not suitable for freezing.

**Flaky Blackcurrant and Apple Slice**

This delicious slice takes a bit of time to prepare because of the flaky pastry used, but is well worth the effort – it just melts in the mouth! This sweet is equally good hot or cold.

    8 oz (225 g) flaky pastry (see p. 140)

1½ lb (725 g) cooking apples, peeled, cored and sliced
2 tablespoons apple juice
4 oz (100 g) blackcurrants — fresh, frozen or bottled
1 teaspoon ground mace
1–2 dessertspoons soft brown sugar
Soya milk to glaze

## Method

- Set oven to Gas 7/220°C/425°F.
- Make the flaky pastry. Wrap and chill for 30 minutes.
- Stew the apples in the apple juice on a low heat for 2–3 minutes until *just softening*. Stir in the blackcurrants, mace and enough sugar to sweeten. Allow to cool.
- Divide the flaky pastry in half. Roll out one half on a well floured board to an oblong approximately 10″ × 6″ (25 × 15cm). Lay on a baking sheet.
- Spread the apple mixture on the pastry leaving a 1″ (2.5 cm) border round the edge.
- Roll out the other piece of pastry to a 10″ × 6″ (25 × 15 cm) oblong. Fold in half lengthways and make slits at 1″ (2.5 cm) intervals along the folded edge leaving a 1″ (2.5 cm) uncut border round the edge. (Figure 5).

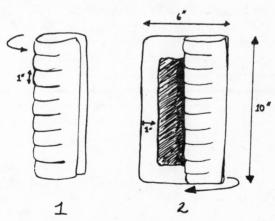

**Figure 5**

- Brush the edges of the base pastry with soya milk then cover the apple mixture with the slit pastry and seal the edges well. Cut the edges with a sharp knife to straighten and 'knock up' with the back of a knife to increase the flakiness.

257

- Brush the soya milk and bake for 2–25 minutes until golden and crisp.
- Serve hot or cold with tofu or nut cream.
- Freeze cooked and thaw to serve. Can be reheated from thawed state in low oven for 30 minutes.


## Baked Bananas

An absolutely delicious and quick pudding to make. A winner with children.

> 4 large bananas
> 1 oz (25 g) dates, chopped
> 1 oz (25 g) toasted flaked almonds
> Rind and juice 1 orange
> Maple syrup to serve

### *Method*

Set oven to Gas 4/180°C/350°F.
Grease a 2 pint (1 litre) ovenproof dish.

- Chop the bananas into chunky pieces and put into the dish with the dates, orange juice and rind. Mix.
- Sprinkle almonds on top, cover with foil and bake for 20 minutes until the bananas are soft and cooked.
- Serve immediately with warm maple syrup or chocolate sauce.
- Not suitable for freezing.


## Rhubarb and Apple Cobbler

This filling dessert makes a nice change from a pie. Any fruits in season may be substituted for the rhubarb and apple.

> 1 lb (500 g) young cherry rhubarb, washed and cut into 1″ (2.5 cm) lengths
> 1 lb (500 g) cooking apples, peeled, cored and sliced
> 4 tablespoons apple juice
> 2 teaspoons cinnamon
> 2–3 dessertspoons soft brown sugar
> 4 oz (100 g) wholemeal flour
> 2 teaspoons baking powder

1 oz (25 g) margarine
1 dessertspoon molasses
½ teaspoon mixed spice
2 fl oz (50 ml) soya milk

## Method

Set oven to Gas 8/230°C/450°F.
Lightly grease a 2 pint (1 litre) ovenproof dish.

- Put the rhubarb and apple in a pan with the apple juice and stew on a low heat for 5 minutes until just beginning to soften.
- Stir in the cinnamon and enough sugar to sweeten to your taste. Cool slightly.
- Rub the margarine into the flour and baking powder until the mixture resembles breadcrumbs. Stir in the mixed spice.
- Add the molasses and enough soya milk from the 2 fl oz (50 ml) to form a moist, firm dough that leaves the sides of the bowl clean. Knead lightly until smooth.
- Pour the apple and rhubarb mixture into the prepared dish.
- Roll the scone mixture out on a well floured board until it is about ½" (1 cm) thick and will fit the top of the fruit. Lay it on top of the fruit. (*Alternatively: cut rounds out of the scone dough with a small fluted cutter and lay these on top of the fruit*).
- Score the top of the scone with a sharp knife to form a criss-cross pattern and brush with the remaining soya milk.
- Bake for 10–15 minutes until the scone is well risen and brown. Serve immediately with soya custard or tofu cream.
- Freezes well raw or cooked. Reheat in a low oven. Allow to thaw if frozen.

## Rice Pudding

A creamy vegan version of the traditional favourite which is highly nutritious.

2 oz (50 g) short-grain brown rice
1 oz (25 g) sugar
1 pint (½ litre) soya milk
¼ pint (150 ml) undiluted Plamil (optional)
1 oz (25 g) margarine
Grated nutmeg

## Method

Set oven to Gas 3/170°C/325°F.
Grease well a 2 pint (1 litre) ovenproof dish using some of the margarine.

- Put the rice, sugar, milk and undiluted Plamil (if using) into the dish and stir gently. The Plamil adds an extra rich creaminess to the pudding.
- Dot the remaining margarine on top of the pudding and bake for 2½–3 hours until thick and creamy. Sprinkle nutmeg on top after 1 hour of cooking.
- If you wish to prevent a skin forming do not dot with margarine. Cover with foil to cook.
- Delicious served with stewed dried fruits especially Hunza apricots.
- Not suitable for freezing.

*Variation:* Add some sultanas after 1 hour of cooking. Cinnamon, mixed spice and vanilla may be used as flavourings instead of nutmeg if preferred.


## Apple and Apricot Turnovers

These delicious flaky triangles can be served hot or cold as a sweet after a meal or a picnic item. (Makes 4)

    4 oz (100 g) flaky pastry
    4 oz (100 g) dried apricots
    ¼ pint (150ml) apple juice
    1 lb (450 g) cooking apples, peeled, cored and finely chopped
    1 teaspoon cinnamon
    Soya milk to glaze


## Method

Set the oven to Gas 7/220°C/425°F.

- Make the flaky pastry as described on page 140. Wrap and chill for 30 minutes.
- Chop the apricots finely and stew in the apple juice on a low heat for 10 minutes until soft and most of the liquid is absorbed.
- Add the cooking apples to the pan and a drop more apple

**Figure 6**

juice if the mixture seems too dry. Cover and simmer for 5 minutes until the apples are softening. Add the cinnamon, stir well and cool.

• Roll the pastry out on a well floured board to a 12″ × 12″ (30 × 30 cm) square. Cut the square in half then in half again to form four 6″ (15 cm) squares. See Fig. 6.

• Divide the apple and apricot mixture into four portions and put each portion onto one half of the four pastry squares.

• Brush the edges of the pastry with soya milk and fold the pastry over the filling to form four triangular parcels. Seal the edges, trim if necessary and 'knock up' the edges with the back of a knife to increase flakiness.

• Make a slit on each turnover, brush with milk and bake for 20 minutes until brown and well risen.

• Serve with soya custard or chocolate sauce.

• Freeze raw and bake from frozen.


## Christmas Pudding

A lovely rich pudding suitable for serving on Christmas Day or Boxing Day depending on how full you feel! This recipe makes one 2 pint (1 litre) or two 1 pint (500 ml) puddings. It is better if made at least 2 months before Christmas and left to mature.

    2 oz (50 g) wholemeal flour
    2 oz (50 g) wholemeal breadcrumbs
    4 oz (100 g) molasses sugar
    4 oz (100 g) raisins
    4 oz (100 g) sultanas
    4 oz (100 g) currants

2 oz (50 g) flaked almonds
2 oz (50 g) Suenut, Broadland vegetable suet or white vegetable fat, grated
1 tablespoon molasses
1 small cooking apple, peeled, cored and grated
1 carrot, grated
Rind and juice 1 small lemon
Rind ½ orange
½ teaspoon mixed spice
½ teaspoon cinnamon
¼ pint (150 ml) orange juice or brandy or a mixture of the two
3–4 tablespoons soya milk


*Method*

Grease well a 2 pint (1 litre) pudding basin or two 1 pint (500 ml) pudding basins.

• Mix all the ingredients together in a bowl adding enough soya milk to form a stiff but moist misture. Stir thoroughly.

• Pile into the prepared basin(s) and smooth over.

• Cover with a piece of greased and pleated greaseproof paper or tinfoil and secure round the bowl with string. (The pleat allows steam to escape).

*To steam:* the pudding can be steamed in a steamer or a pan of water depending on which is available. The 2 pint (1 litre) pudding will take 8–9 hours to steam and the 1 pint (500 ml) puddings 4–5 hours to steam. They should be firm and very dark in colour when they are done. Top up the water in the pans regularly to ensure they do not boil dry.

*To pressure cook:* the puddings cook more quickly in a pressure cooker. Steam them initially for 20 minutes in the pressure cooker with no weights on. Then bring to pressure and fix the 15 lb (HIGH) weights. Steam on 15 lb (HIGH) pressure for 1½ hours (1 pint/500 ml pudding) or 2½ hours (2 pint/1 litre pudding).

*To store:* cool the puddings and wrap them so as to exclude air. Store in a cool, dark place for at least 2 months. They can be spiked and more spirit added if desired.

*To reheat:* steam the puddings for 2 hours (1 pint/500 ml) or 3 hours (2 pint/1 litre) on the day, before serving, or pressure cook on 15 lb (HIGH) pressure for 30 minutes.

Serve with nutcream, soya custard, fruity nutcream, orange sauce or apricot sauce.


## Apple and Raisin Pancakes

These lovely filled pancakes make a very impressive dinner party sweet. They can be prepared in advance and heated through just before serving to avoid last minute panics.

(For 8)
*Batter:*
    4 oz (100 g) 100% wholemeal flour
    1 heaped tablespoon soya flour
    1 heaped tablespoon gram (chickpea) flour
    12 fl oz (325 ml) soya milk
    1 tablespoon oil
    1 teaspoon baking powder
    Oil to fry

*Filling:*
    1 lb (500 g) cooking apples
    2 tablespoons orange juice
    Rind 1 orange
    3 oz (75 g) raisins
    Pinch mixed spice

### *Method*

• Mix the flour, soya flour, gram flour and baking powder together in a bowl. Add the soya milk a little at a time beating thoroughly to make a smooth batter. Whisk in the oil. (Alternatively whizz all the batter ingredients together in a blender for 1–2 minutes until smooth).
• Leave the batter to stand for 30 minutes in a cool place.
• Peel, core and slice the apples. Place in a pan with the raisins and orange juice.
• Stew on a low heat for 5 minutes, stirring occasionally until the apple is puréed and the raisins soft.
• Stir in the spice and the orange rind. Cool.
• Whisk the batter again.
• Oil a frying pan or omelette pan and heat until the pan is hot (not smoking). Spoon about 2 fl oz (50 ml) batter into a pan and tilt so the batter covers the base of the pan. (It should sizzle as it hits the hot fat).

- Cook for 1 minute until brown, then ease with a palette knife, flip the pancake over and cook the other side until brown.
- Slip the pancake onto a sheet of greaseproof paper or kitchen roll. Re-oil the pan, return to heat and cook the remaining pancakes. (Add a drop of oil in between each one).
- When all 8 pancakes are cooked they can be filled. Put about 1 tablespoon apple filling on the edge of each one and roll it up to enclose the filling.
- Put the filled pancakes on an oiled tray and warm through, covered with foil for about 15–20 minutes Gas 4/180°C/350°F.
- Serve immediately with soya custard, soya icecream, nut-cream or pineapple sauce.
- Can be frozen on the tray, then thawed and warmed through. Alternatively, freeze the pancakes without the filling, putting a piece of greaseproof paper in between each one. Thaw and fill.

## Almond and Apricot Pancakes

These luxurious pancakes make a lovely dessert but are probably best reserved for special occasions or entertaining as the filling is a little bit more expensive than most recipes.

(For 8)

*Batter:*
>4 oz (100 g) 100% wholemeal flour
>1 heaped tablespoon soya flour
>1 heaped tablespoon gram (chickpea) flour
>12 fl oz (325 ml) soya milk
>1 tablespoon oil
>1 teaspoon baking powder
>1 teaspoon mixed spice
>Oil to fry

*Filling:*
>8 oz (225 g) ground almonds
>4 oz (100 g) melted margarine
>4 oz (100 g) dried apricots, chopped
>½ pint (275 ml) orange juice

## Method

- Mix the flour, soya flour, gram flour, baking powder and spice together in a bowl. Add the soya milk a little at a time, beating thoroughly to make a smooth batter. Whisk in the oil. (Alternatively whizz all the batter ingredients together in a blender for 1–2 minutes until smooth).
- Leave the batter to stand in a cool place for 30 minutes.
- Stew the apricots in the orange juice for 10 minutes until they are soft and plump and the juice has reduced and thickened.
- Stir in the almonds and melted margarine and mix thoroughly to a stiff paste.
- Whisk the batter again.
- Oil a frying pan or omelette pan and heat until the pan is hot (not smoking). Spoon about 2 fl oz (50 ml) batter into the pan and tilt so the batter covers the base of the pan (it should sizzle as it hits the hot oil).
- Cook for 1 minute until brown, then ease with a palette knife, flip the pancake over and cook the other side until brown.
- Slip the pancake onto a sheet of greaseproof paper or kitchen roll. Re-oil the pan, return to the heat and cook the remaining pancakes (adding a drop of oil in between each one).
- When all 8 pancakes are cooked they can be filled. Put about one tablespoon almond filling on the edge of each pancake and roll it up to enclose the filling.
- Put the filled pancakes on an oiled tray and warm through, covered with foil for about 15–20 minutes (Gas 4/180°C/350°F).
- Serve immediately with orange sauce or soya ice-cream.
- Can be frozen on the tray, then thawed and warmed through. Alternatively freeze the pancakes without the filling, putting a piece of greaseproof paper in between each one. Thaw and fill.

# COLD SWEETS

There are a variety of things you can use to decorate cold sweets and make them attractive. These are listed below with instructions for preparation where necessary.

---

*Fruit*
Sliced or whole fruits are one of the best decorations for cold sweets as they are so colourful and easy to prepare. Try strawberries, raspberries, blackcurrants, cherries, kiwi fruit, nectarines or peaches, mandarin oranges, pineapple, etc.

*Coconut*
Dessicated or shredded coconut can be sprinkled on mousses, whips and fools. It can be toasted under a grill for 5 minutes or in the oven for 5 minutes on a baking tray (Gas 4/180°C/350°F) to brown it slightly.

*Nuts*
Chopped or flaked nuts (especially almonds and walnuts) can be used as for coconut. They can be toasted in the same way to make them brown and give a better flavour.

*Chocolate*
There are a few varieties of vegan chocolate which can be used to decorate sweets. Kake Brand plain cooking chocolate; Plamil chocolate and non-dairy Carob bar; Waitrose own-brand plain chocolate; Terry's bitter chocolate and Itona's chunky bean-milk bar are all vegan. Chocolate can be either grated on a coarse grater or pared with a vegetable peeler to make curls for decorating sweets.

*Cream*

Home-made vegan creams do not whip very successfully but if you wanted to pipe swirls of cream on a dessert you could use Sainsbury's own brand non-dairy cream, which will whip. It is made from vegetable oils but contains various additives so may not be acceptable to some vegans.

## Vegan Mincemeat

This is my recipe for mincemeat which I use every Christmas. It is very easy to make and infinitely nicer than any bought varieties. Use to make mince pies, mincemeat tarts etc.

(Makes 10 × 1 lb (450 g) jars)
    1 lb (450 g) raisins
    1 lb (450 g) sultanas
    1 lb (450 g) currants
    1 lb (450 g) molasses sugar
    1 lb (450 g) chopped walnuts
    8 oz (225 g) grated white vegetable fat e.g. Suenut, Nutter, white Flora or Broadland vegetable suet etc.
    1 lb (450 g) grated cooking apple
    Rind and juice 1 lemon
    Rind and juice 1 orange
    1 teaspoon cinnamon
    $\frac{1}{2}$ teaspoon mace or nutmeg
    $\frac{1}{2}$ teaspoon mixed spice
    3 tablespoons brandy (optional)
    $\frac{1}{2}$ pint (275 ml) apple juice (approx.)

*Method*

• Mix all the ingredients in a large bowl and moisten with enough apple juice to make a wet mixture (the wetter the better).

• Cover and leave to stand in a cool place for 2 days. Stir 2 or 3 times a day to coat all the ingredients. (All the fruit should be well swollen).

• Pack firmly into 10 clean 1 lb (450 g) jars leaving a 1" (2.5 cm) space at the top.

• Cover with jam pot covers or screw on lids and store in a cool place for 2 months before using. Refrigerate once opened.

• As the mincemeat contains no preservatives it is best used within 4 months of making.

## Mincemeat and Apple Flan

A lovely light Christmas sweet that is a popular change from Christmas pudding which many find too heavy after a rich nut roast. If you make your own mincemeat you can eat this all year round. (Serves 4–6.)

> 4 oz (100 g) nut pastry made with almonds
> 3–4 tablespoons homemade or proprietary vegan mincemeat
> 1 medium cooking apple
> 1 tablespoon low-sugar apricot jam or marmalade
> 1 teaspoon orange juice

### Method

Set oven to Gas 6/200°C/400°F.

• Make the pastry. Roll out to fit an 8″ (20 cm) pie dish or flan ring. Trim edges.
• Spread the mincemeat on the base of the flan and smooth over.
• Peel, core and slice the apple thinly. Arrange the slices on top of the mincemeat, layering each one to overlap each other slightly to give a 'fan' effect.
• Bake for 20–25 minutes until the pastry is cooked and apple slices are tinged brown. Cool.
• Melt the jam and orange juice together then brush over the top of the flan until shiny.
• Serve chilled with nutcream or tofu cream.
• Can be frozen raw and then cooked from frozen and glazed or frozen cooked. If frozen cooked it may need to be reglazed as the glaze tends to soak into the apples.

## French Apple Flan

This chilled tangy flan is very attractive as a dinner party sweet. (Serves 4–6).

4 oz (100 g) nut pastry
3 large cooking apples
Knob margarine
Rind and juice 1 orange
$\frac{1}{2}$ teaspoon mixed spice
1 tablespoon low-sugar apricot jam or marmalade
1 teaspoon orange juice

## Method

Set oven to Gas 6/200°C/400°F.

• Make the pastry. Roll out to fit an 8″ (20 cm) pie dish or flan ring. Trim edges.
• Peel and core the apples. Roughly chop 2 of them and stew for 5–10 minutes in the juice from the orange and the margarine until a thick purée is formed. Beat until smooth then add the spice and orange rind.
• Spread the apple purée on the base of the flan.
• Slice the remaining apple thinly and arrange the slices on top of the purée layering each one to overlap the other to give a 'fan' effect.
• Bake for 20–25 minutes until the pastry is cooked and the apple slices are tinged brown, Cool.
• Melt the jam and orange juice together then brush over the top of the flan until shiny.
• Serve chilled with fruity nutcream or tofu cream.
• Can be frozen raw then cooked from frozen and glazed or frozen cooked. If frozen cooked it may need to be reglazed as the glaze tends to soak into the fruit on freezing.

## Date and Apricot Flan

This attractive flan is naturally sweet because of the dried fruit and is also rich in iron. Nice as a sweet or a picnic item. (Serves 6)

4 oz (100 g) nut pastry
4 oz (100 g) dried apricots, chopped finely
4 oz (100 g) stoned dates, chopped finely
$\frac{3}{4}$ pint (450 ml) orange or apple juice
$\frac{1}{2}$ teaspoon mixed spice
Rind 1 orange

*Method*

Set oven to Gas 6/200°C/400°F.

- Make the pastry. Reserve a small ball of it and roll the rest on a well floured board to fit an 8″ (20 cm) flan ring or pie dish.
- Put the apricots in a pan with the juice and stew, covered, on a low heat for 15 minutes until soft and swollen. Add the dates to the pan and continue to stew for 5 minutes until the fruit can be mashed to a purée.
- Stir in the spice and orange rind and spread into the base of the prepared pastry case.
- Roll out the reserved ball of pastry thinly and cut into 10 strips ½″ (1 cm) wide. Cut to fit the tart and lay 5 across one way and then 5 across the other to form a lattice over the fruit. Moisten the ends of the strips with water and stick to the pastry base around the rim.
- Bake for 15 minutes until the pastry is golden. Cool.
- Serve with nutcream, soya dessert, soya icecream etc.
- Freeze unbaked and bake from frozen.

## Crunchy Almond and Strawberry Flan

This delicious sweet consists of a crunchy biscuit base with a smooth almond filling and fresh strawberry topping. An impressive summer dessert. (Serves 4–6).

4 oz (100 g) vegan digestive biscuits (e.g. *Mitchelhills, Doves Farm, Raskusens, McVities Wholemeal Biscuits*)
2 oz (50 g) margarine
8 oz (225 g) *silken* tofu, drained
3 oz (75 g) ground almonds
2 oz (50 g) stoned dates
4 tablespoons apple juice
½ teaspoon ground cardamom
12 oz (350 g) fresh strawberries, washed and hulled
1 tablespoon no-sugar strawberry jam

*Method*

Set oven to Gas 4/180°C/350°F.
Grease an 8″ (20 cm) pie dish.

- Crush the digestive biscuits in a plastic bag with a rolling pin until fine. Melt the margarine and stir in the crushed biscuits.
- Pour the biscuit mixture into the prepared tin and then press down firmly with the back of a spoon to completely line the base and sides of the tin.
- Stew the dates in the apple juice for 5 minutes until soft and mushy, then mash to a smooth purée.
- Put the date purée in a liquidizer with the almonds, tofu and cardamom. Whizz until thick and creamy.
- Pour into the biscuit case, smooth over and bake for 20 minutes until set and golden brown. Cool.
- Slice the strawberries in half and lay on top of the cooled flan to completely cover the almond mixture.
- Melt the jam with 2 teaspoons water on a low heat until runny. Brush over the strawberries with a pastry brush to glaze them.
- Chill the flan for 2 hours before serving.
- Not suitable for freezing.

*Variation:* Other soft fruits can be used in place of the strawberries e.g. raspberries, loganberries, blackcurrants, peaches, nectarines, plums etc. For the orange fruits such as peaches, use apricot jam as a glaze rather than strawberry.


## Banana and Coconut Flan

A delicious creamy flan that is ideal as a summer buffet party sweet although it can be served all year round! The flan is quite rich so will probably serve 6 to 8 people.

4 oz (100 g) shortcrust pastry
2 large ripe bananas
3 oz (75 g) ground cashew nuts
4 oz (100 g) solid coconut cream (e.g. Sharwoods)
¼ pint (150 ml) boiling water
8 oz (225 g) *silken* tofu
1 teaspoon ground cardamom
1 teaspoon vanilla essence
Strawberries, kiwi fruit or vegan chocolate curls to decorate

## Method

Set oven to Gas 6/200°C/400°F.

• Make pastry as described on page 138. Roll out on a well floured board and use to line an 8″ (20 cm) pie dish or flan ring. Trim edges.
• Prick the pastry case all over with a fork and bake 'blind' (empty) for 10–15 minutes until golden brown. Allow to cool.
• Dissolve the coconut cream in the boiling water to form a smooth cream.
• Put the coconut cream, cashew nuts, tofu, cardamom and vanilla in a liquidizer and whizz until thick and smooth.
• Slice the bananas into the cooled pastry case and spread the coconut mixture on top. Chill for at least 2 hours before serving.
• Decorate with half strawberries, sliced kiwi fruit or chocolate curls.
• Not suitable for freezing.

### Chocolate Tofu and Banana Flan

This delicious flan looks and tastes utterly wicked but in fact, because tofu is used, it is low in saturated fat and has no cholesterol. Extremely popular with children, the chocolate topping doubles up as a whip if served in individual glasses.

> 4 oz (100 g) nut pastry
> 2 bananas
> 10 oz (275 g) *silken* tofu, drained
> 2 oz dates
> Rind and juice 1 orange
> 1 tablespoon carob or cocoa powder
> Flaked almonds, dessicated coconut or vegan chocolate curls to decorate

## Method

Set oven to Gas 6/200°C/400°F.

• Make the pastry as described on page 139 and roll out to fit an 8″ (20 cm) pie plate or flan ring. Trim edges. Prick all over with a fork and bake for 10–15 minutes until golden and cooked. Cool.
• Grate the rind from the orange and put into a liquidizer with the tofu.

- Squeeze the juice from the orange and make up to 3 tablespoons with water. Simmer the dates in this liquid for a few minutes until soft. Mash with a fork to a smooth purée.
- Add the date purée to the tofu and orange rind in the liquidizer.
- Mix the carob or cocoa with 2 tablespoons boiling water to form a paste and add to all the other ingredients in the liquidizer.
- Whizz the tofu, orange rind, date purée and cocoa paste in the liquidizer until thick and creamy.
- Slice the bananas into the cooled pastry case and spread the chocolate cream on top. Chill for 1 hour.
- Sprinkle almonds, coconut or chocolate curls on top before serving.
- Not suitable for freezing as the tofu goes very chewy.

*Variation:* Use any soft fruit in place of banana.


## Apricot or Date Slice I

These quick and easy slices are ideal as a cold sweet or lunch box treat. Packed with iron and vitamins, the dried fruit is naturally sweet — a good way to wean children off commercially produced confectionery. (For 12 slices)

8 oz (225 g) wholemeal shortcrust or nut pastry
8 oz (225 g) dried apricots or stoned dates
1 teaspoon cinnamon
Rind 1 orange
½ pint (275 ml) apple juice
Soya milk to glaze


### *Method*

Set oven to Gas 6/200°C/400°F.
Lightly grease a 9″ × 12″ (23 × 30 cm) swiss roll tin or similar baking tray.

- Put the apricots or dates in a pan with the apple juice and bring to the boil. Lower heat and simmer gently for 20 minutes (dates) or 30 minutes (apricots) until the fruit is swollen and mushy. Add water during cooking if the fruit is drying out too much.
- Mash or liquidize the fruit to a soft, moist purée with the

orange rind and cinnamon. Cool slightly.
• Make the pastry. Divide in half. Roll one half into an oblong that will fit the base of the prepared tin. Press into tin.
• Spread the fruit purée on the pastry.
• Roll the remaining pastry to fit over the top of the fruit. Press down lightly and trim any surplus.
• Prick all over with a fork, brush with soya milk and bake for 20–25 minutes until pastry is well browned.
• Cut into 12 bars while warm and cool in tin. Store in an airtight container. Keep 3–4 days.
• Freeze well cooked or uncooked.

## Apricot or Date Slice II

These take slightly longer to prepare than the first version and are best served in a bowl as a sweet because the crunchy topping is very crumbly. They are extremely nutritious. (For 12 slices).

4 oz (100 g) wholemeal shortcrust or nut pastry
8 oz (225 g) dried apricots or stoned dates
1 teaspoon mixed spice
Rind 1 orange
½ pint (275 ml) orange juice
6 oz (175 g) margarine
4 tablespoons malt extract
8 oz (225 g) rolled oats
4 oz (100 g) wholemeal flour
2 oz (50 g) sunflower seeds

*Method*

Set oven to Gas 6/200°C/400°F.
Lightly grease a 9″ × 12″ (23 × 30 cm) swiss roll tin or similar baking tray.

• Put the apricots or dates in a pan with the orange juice and bring to the boil. Lower heat and simmer gently for 20 minutes (dates) or 30 minutes (apricots) until the fruit is swollen and mushy. Add water during cooking if the fruit is drying out too much.
• Mash or liquidize the fruit to a smooth, moist purée with the orange rind and spice. Cool slightly.

274

- Make the pastry. Roll out into an oblong that will fit the base of the prepared tin. Press into the tin.
- Melt the margarine and malt extract together until runny. (To measure the malt extract, dip the spoon in boiling water — this prevents it sticking too much).
- Add the oats, flour and seeds to the malt mixture and stir well until thoroughly mixed.
- Spread the apricot or date purée on the pastry base.
- Sprinkle the crumble mixture on top of the fruit to cover completely and press down very lightly.
- Bake for 20 minutes or until crumble topping is brown and crisp.
- Cut into 12 bars while warm and cool in tin. Serve with nutcream, soya ice cream, soya dessert or coconut cream. Keep 4–5 days in an airtight container.
- Freezes well uncooked or cooked.

## Mocha Almond and Raisin Ice-cream

This heavenly ice-cream is very easy to make. As bananas are used for the base, the texture is very smooth and creamy so there is no need to stir it when partially frozen or use an elaborate ice-cream maker. (For 4 portions).

4 large ripe bananas
6 oz (175 g) ground cashew nuts
1 dessertspoon carob powder
1 dessertspoon Barley cup or coffee powder
1 tablespoon warm water
3 oz (75 g) almonds
3 oz (75 g) raisins

*Method*

Set freezer to 'fast freeze' or coldest setting.

- Roughly chop the almonds, place on a baking tray and roast in a low oven Gas 4/180°C/350°F for 10 minutes, shaking frequently. Cool.
- Dissolve the carob and Barleycup in the water and pour into a liquidizer. Add the bananas and cashew nuts. Whizz until thick and creamy.
- Stir in the almonds and raisins. Pour into a 2 pint (1 litre)

container with a lid and freeze for at least 4 hours before serving.
• Remove from freezer for 10 minutes before serving to soften slightly.


## Strawberry Ice-cream

A lovely creamy ice-cream that makes the most of strawberries when they are cheap and in season. Any soft fruits may be substituted — try blackcurrants, raspberries or loganberries. (For 4 portions).

8 fl oz (225 ml) undiluted, sweetened Plamil
2 fl oz (50 ml) water
3 tablespoons sunflower oil
3 tablespoons maple syrup
8 oz (225 g) ripe strawberries
1 ripe banana

### Method

Set freezer to 'fast-freeze'.

• Put all ingredients into a liquidizer and whizz until smooth and creamy.
• Pour into a shallow tray and freeze for 1 hour. Remove from freezer and whisk with a balloon whisk or fork to break up any large ice-crystals.
• Pour into a bowl and freeze for at least 3 hours before serving. Remove from freezer 10 minutes before serving to soften slightly.


## Brown Bread Ice-cream

This is a vegan adaptation of a very unusual Victorian recipe. This ice-cream has a lovely rich caramel-toffee flavour and can be served on its own or as a topping for fruit. (For 4 portions).

$\frac{3}{4}$ pint (450 ml) undiluted, sweetened Plamil
$4\frac{1}{2}$ oz (112 g) stale, crustless, wholemeal breadcrumbs
$4\frac{1}{2}$ oz (112 g) molasses sugar

2 teaspoons vanilla essence

## Method

Set oven to Gas 6/200°C/400°F. Set freezer to 'fast-freeze'. Lightly oil a baking tray.

• Mix the breadcrumbs and sugar together and place on the prepared tray. Put in the oven for 5 minutes until the crumbs are well browned and the sugar has caramelized. Cool.
• Break the caramel/crumb mixture into small pieces and put in a liquidizer with the Plamil and vanilla essence. Whizz until creamy.
• Pour into a shallow tray, cover and freeze for one hour.
• Remove from freezer and whisk with a balloon whisk or fork to break up any large ice crystals.
• Pour into a bowl and refreeze for at least 3 hours before serving. Remove from freezer 10 minutes before serving to soften slightly.

## Raspberry Mousse

A tangy light mousse that is ideal as a sweet after a filling main course. Any summer fruits can be substituted for the raspberries if they are not available e.g. strawberries, redcurrants, blackcurrants, cherries, peaches, nectarines, plums. (For 4 sundae glasses)

1 rounded teaspoon agar powder
$\frac{1}{2}$ pint (275 ml) apple juice
1 lb (450 g) raspberries, washed
3 oz (75 g) ground cashew nuts or almonds
2 tablespoons light muscavado sugar
Fruit to decorate e.g. kiwi fruit slices or orange twists

## Method

• Put the apple juice in a pan and sprinkle the agar on top. Bring to the boil and simmer gently for one minute until the agar has dissolved. Cool slightly.
• Pour the agar mixture into a liquidizer with all the other ingredients. Whizz until smooth.

- Pour into 4 individual glasses or one bowl and chill for 2 hours until set. Decorate with fruit of your choice.
- Not suitable for freezing.


## Apricot and Banana Whip

A deliciously rich and creamy whip that is ideal for a dinner party dessert. (For 4 sundae glasses)

6 oz (175 g) dried apricots
½ pint (275 ml) orange juice
1 large ripe banana
4 oz (100 g) *silken* tofu, drained
½ teaspoonful mixed spice
Flaked almonds or vegan chocolate curls to decorate


### *Method*

- Stew the apricots in the orange juice on a low heat for 30 minutes, until plump and most of the juice has been absorbed.
- Put into a liquidizer with all the other ingredients and whizz until smooth and creamy. Pour into 4 sundae glasses and chill for 2 hours before serving. Decorate with almonds or chocolate curls.
- Can be frozen. Thaw overnight in the fridge before serving.


## Tropical Fruit Whip

This heavenly, smooth dessert has a lovely rich coconut flavour and is ideal after a spicy main course such as curry. (For 4 sundae glasses).

8 oz (225 g) *silken* tofu
2 large ripe bananas
4 oz (100 g) solid coconut cream (e.g. Sharwoods)
4 oz (100 g) fresh or tinned (unsweetened) pineapple, chopped finely
Toasted flaked almonds to decorate

278

## Method

- Dissolve the coconut cream in ¼ pint (150 ml) boiling water to form a smooth paste.
- Put the coconut cream, tofu and bananas in a liquidizer and whizz for 2–3 minutes until smooth and creamy.
- Stir in the chopped pineapple and pour the whip into 4 glasses.
- Chill for 2 hours before serving. Decorate with almonds.
- Not suitable for freezing.


## Rhubarb and Orange Fool

This tangy fool is delicious served after a heavy main course. Low in fat and cholesterol free. Young cherry rhubarb has the best flavour and is not too 'tart'. (For 4 sundae glasses)

> 12 oz (350 g) young cherry rhubarb
> 8 oz (225 g) *silken* tofu
> Rind and juice 1 orange
> 3 tablespoons light brown sugar
> ½ teaspoon ground ginger
> Toasted flaked almonds or vegan chocolate curls to decorate

## Method

- Wash the rhubarb, cut off any green leaves and chop into small pieces. Put in a pan with the juice from the orange and stew on a low heat for 5 minutes until soft. Beat to a smooth purée. Cool slightly.
- Put the rhubarb puree, tofu, orange rind, sugar and ginger into a liquidizer or blender. Whizz for a few minutes until smooth and creamy.
- Pour into 4 sundae glasses and chill for 2 hours before serving. Decorate with almonds or chocolate curls.
- Not suitable for freezing.


## Fruity Tofu Whip

This lovely creamy whip makes a light, tangy sweet that is

279

ideal after a rich main course. Any soft fruits in season may be used. (For 4 sundae glasses).

> 3 oz (75 g) ground cashew nuts
> 8 oz (225 g) *silken* tofu
> 6 oz (175 g) soft fruit e.g. strawberries, raspberries, blackcurrants, cherries, plums, apricots, peaches etc.
> 1 large ripe banana
> Rind and juice 1 orange
> Fresh fruit or nuts to decorate

### Method

• Put all the ingredients into a liquidizer or food processor and whizz for 2–3 minutes until smooth and creamy.
• Pour into 4 sundae glasses and chill for 2 hours before serving. Decorate with fruit or chopped nuts.
• Not suitable for freezing.

## Tropical Fruit Jelly

Any fruits can be used to make this unusual vegan jelly. Can be used as a base for trifle with soya custard and non-dairy cream on top.

> 1 pint (500 ml) unsweetened tropical fruit juice (a mixture of banana, mango, pineapple, guava, passion fruit, etc.) or any other fruit juice
> 2 rounded teaspoons agar powder
> 1 lb (450 g) fruits chopped e.g. pineapple, bananas, kiwi, raspberries, strawberries, peaches, etc.

### Method

• Pour the juice into a pan and sprinkle in the agar powder.
• Bring to the boil and simmer gently until the agar has dissolved.
• Put the fruit into a serving dish or 4 individual dishes and pour the jelly over the top. Cool slightly before refrigerating until set (about one hour).
• Serve alone or with nutcream, soya ice-cream, soya dessert, etc.

# Creamy Orange and Banana Jelly

The addition of *silken* tofu to a basic jelly mixture makes a lovely creamy 'milk' jelly that is very popular with children and a good way to increase protein intake.

> 1 pint (500 ml) unsweetened orange juice
> Rind 1 orange
> 4 oz (100 g) *silken* tofu, drained
> 2 rounded teaspoons agar powder
> 4 ripe bananas

## *Method*

• Pour the orange juice into a pan and sprinkle in the agar powder.
• Bring to the boil and simmer gently until the agar has dissolved.
• Put the *silken* tofu into a liquidizer with the orange rind and whizz to form a smooth cream. Add the jelly and whizz again to mix thoroughly.
• Slice the bananas into a serving dish or 4 individual dishes and pour the jelly over the top. Cool slightly before refrigerating until set (about one hour).
• Serve alone or with nutcream, soya icecream etc.

# Baked Tofu Cheesecake

This no cholesterol, high protein cheesecake is so deliciously creamy it is hard to believe no dairy produce is used. Use your favourite fruits to create a very impressive dessert. (Serves 6—8). *This recipe is dedicated to Jackie.*

*Base:*
> 4 oz (100 g) vegan digestive biscuits (e.g. *Mitchelhills*, *Doves Farm*, *Raskusens*, *McVities Wholemeal Biscuits*)
> 2 oz (50 g) margarine

*Topping:*
> 12 oz (350 g) *firm* tofu
> ¼ pint (150 ml) apple juice
> 1 large ripe banana
> 1 dessertspoon tahini

Rind and juice 1 large lemon
2 oz (50 g) stoned dates
3 tablespoons water
1 teaspoon vanilla essence
½ teaspoon mixed spice
Any fresh fruits to decorate e.g. Kiwi, mandarins, grapes, strawberries etc.

## *Method*

Set oven to Gas 4/180°C/350°F.
Lightly grease a 7″ (18 cm) round loose-bottomed cake tin.

• Crush the digestives in a plastic bag with a rolling pin until fine and crumbly. Melt the margarine add the biscuits. Mix well.
• Press digestive base into the prepared tin and smooth over.
• Stew the dates in the water and lemon juice for 5 minutes until soft and mushy. Mash with a fork.
• ·Put the tofu, lemon rind, date purée, apple juice, tahini, banana, vanilla essence and spice in a liquidizer. Whizz for 2–3 minutes until thick, smooth and creamy.
• Pour the tofu cream onto the digestive base and smooth over.
• Bake for 30–40 minutes until the tofu is pale brown and well set. Cool in the tin.
• Run a knife round the edge of the cheesecake and push up the base of the tin to release it. Put on a serving plate and decorate with fruits. Chill thoroughly before serving.
• Not suitable for freezing.

*Variation*: *Silken tofu* may be used instead of firm tofu to give a softer, smoother texture. *Silken* tofu takes 45–50 minutes to set.

Instead of fresh fruit, *tinned fruit* (no sugar type) may be used to decorate. Strain off the juice and add 2 teaspoons cornflour or arrowroot. Stir well, then bring to the boil and simmer until thick. Add the fruit to the thickened juice, cool, then spread on the cheesecake. Blackcurrants or raspberries are especially delicious.

# Crunchy Apple Slice

This delicious crunchy dessert is tangy smooth on the inside and crunchy on the outside. Ideal as a dinner party dessert and very popular with children. (Serves 6–8).

2 lb (900 g) cooking apples, peeled, cored and sliced
7 oz (200 g) margarine
½ teaspoon nutmeg
Rind 1 orange
6 oz (175 g) wholemeal flour
6 oz (175 g) malt extract
6 oz (175 g) toasted wheatflakes, cornflakes or bran-flakes
2 oz (50 g) sunflower seeds
1 teaspoon mixed spice

## *Method*

Heat oven to Gas 6/200°C/400°F.
Grease a 7" (18 cm) round, loose-bottomed cake tin.

•   Melt 1 oz (25 g) of the margarine and add the apples. Cover and stew the apples in the margarine on a low heat for 5 minutes until they can be beaten to a smooth purée. Stir regularly during cooking to prevent burning.
•   Stir the nutmeg and orange rind into the apple purée and put to one side.
•   Melt the remaining 6 oz (175 g) margarine with the malt extract until runny. Stir in the flour, wheatflakes, sunflower seeds and spice. Mix well.
•   Put half the wheatflake mixture on the base of the prepared tin and press down fairly firmly.
•   Spread the apple purée on top. Then cover with the remaining wheatflake mixture and press down lightly to cover the apple.
•   Bake for 15–20 minutes until well browned. Cool in the tin.
•   Run a knife around the tin to loosen the slice then push up the base to turn it out. Put on a plate and chill for 2 hours before serving.
•   Serve with nutcream, soya icecream etc. Store in an airtight container in the fridge.
•   To freeze, turn the slice out and freeze without slicing up. Thaw and chill before serving.

## Apple and Hazelnut Galette

Galettes originated in France and are thin round 'cakes' made from pastry, yeasted dough or shortcake. My version is made from 2 layers of crispy hazelnut shortcake sandwiched together with a tangy apple filling. A delicious dinner party dessert.

4 oz (100 g) margarine
2 oz (50 g) light muscavado sugar
3 oz (75 g) ground hazelnuts
4½ oz (112 g) flour
1 lb (450 g) cooking apples, peeled, cored and chopped
Rind and juice 1 orange
2 oz (50 g) sultanas
1 teaspoon mace

### *Method*

Set oven to Gas 5/190°C/375°F.
Grease two 7″ (18 cm) sandwich tins.

• Cream 3 oz (75 g) of the margarine with the sugar until light and fluffy. Stir in the hazelnuts and flour to form a crumbly mixture.
• Divide the shortcake mixture between the 2 tins and press down firmly to form 2 thin biscuits. Mark each into 6 portions (this will make serving easier later).
• Bake the shortcakes for 10 minutes. Do not brown. Cool in the tins.
• Put the apples, orange rind and juice, sultanas, mace and the remaining 1 oz (25 g) margarine in a pan. Stew on a low heat for 5 minutes until the apples can be beaten to a smooth purée. Cool.
• Run a knife round the shortcake and tip out gently so as not to break the portions. Put one on a plate and spread the cooled apple mixture on top.
• Put the second shortcake on top of the apple, lining up the portion markings with the bottom shortcake.
• Chill before serving with nutcream, soya ice-cream, soya dessert or tofu cream.
• Open freeze then pack in a plastic bag. Thaw in the fridge and serve.

# Banana and Coconut Charlotte

This rich, delicious sweet is easy to make and requires no baking. Serve chilled for a luxurious dinner party treat.

6 oz (175 g) fresh wholemeal breadcrumbs
3 oz (75 g) ground almonds
3 oz (75 g) margarine
Rind 1 orange
1 dessertspoon soft brown sugar
4 large, ripe bananas
4 oz (100 g) solid coconut cream (e.g. Sharwoods)
$\frac{1}{4}$ pint (150 ml) boiling water

## *Method*

Lightly grease a 2 pint (1 litre) dish.

• Melt the margarine and fry the breadcrumbs on a low heat for 5 minutes, until brown and crispy. Stir regularly to prevent burning.
• Stir in the almonds, sugar and orange rind.
• Dissolve the coconut cream in the boiling water to form a smooth, thick 'milk'.
• Mash the bananas to a smooth purée and stir in the coconut cream.
• Put a layer of breadcrumb mixture on the bottom of the dish and spread half the banana mixture on top. Cover with another layer of crumbs, then the rest of the banana and finally crumbs.
• Chill for $1\frac{1}{2}$–2 hours before serving. Moist enough to serve on its own but may be served with soya ice-cream, undiluted Plamil or tofu cream.
*Variation:* Serve in 4 individual glasses by building up layers of crumbs and banana. It is nice served like this for a dinner party.
• Not suitable for freezing.


## Nectarine and Apricot Shortcake

A nutty shortcake base topped with nectarines and apricot-flavoured 'cream' make this an ideal summer dessert. Serves 6.

*Base*

2 oz (50 g) margarine
1 oz (25 g) light muscavado sugar
1½ oz (37 g) ground almonds
2½ oz (62 g) flour

*Topping*

2 large or 4 small nectarines, stoned and sliced
6 oz (175 g) *silken* tofu
1 ripe banana
2 tablespoons no-sugar or reduced-sugar apricot jam
Vegan chocolate curls to decorate

**Method**

Set oven to Gas 5/190°C/375°F.
Grease a 7″ (18 cm) sandwich tin.

• Cream the margarine and sugar together until smooth then stir in the flour and nuts. Work to a crumbly mixture with the fingers.
• Press the shortcake mixture into the prepared tin with the back of a spoon until firm. Divide into 6 portions with a knife.
• Bake for 10 minutes. Do not brown. Allow to cool.
• Put the tofu, banana and jam into a liquidizer and whizz until smooth and creamy. Chill for 30 minutes in the fridge to set slightly.
• Run a knife round the cooled shortcake and tip out carefully onto a serving plate.
• Cover with the sliced nectarines then spread the chilled apricot mixture on top to cover the nectarines. Sprinkle the chocolate curls on top and chill for 1 hour before serving.
• Not suitable for freezing.


**Treacle Tart**

This version of a traditional sweet uses maple syrup instead of white sugar syrup and is consequently healthier and not as sweet as the traditional tart. Very quick and easy to make. (Serves 4–6).

4 oz (100 g) shortcrust pastry

3 oz (75 g) wholemeal breadcrumbs
Rind 1 lemon
8 oz (225 g) maple syrup
¼ teaspoon ground ginger

## Method

Set oven to Gas 6/200°C/400°F.

• Make the pastry according to the instructions on page 138. Reserve a small ball of it and roll the rest on a well floured board to fit an 8″ (20 cm) pie dish or flan ring. Trim to fit and reserve trimmings.
• Mix the breadcrumbs, lemon rind, maple syrup and ginger together. Pour into the prepared pastry case.
• Roll the reserved pastry out thinly and cut into 10 strips ½″ (1 cm) wide. Cut to fit the tart and lay 5 across one way and then 5 across the other to form a lattice over the syrup filling. Moisten the ends with water and stick to the pastry base around the rim.
• Bake for 10–15 minutes until the pastry is golden and the filling has set.
• Serve cold with coconut or nutcream.
• Bake and freeze after cooling, thaw and serve.

## Apple Bakewell Tart

This is a delicious wholefood, vegan, no-sugar version of a very traditional favourite. Apples are used instead of jam which gives the tart a pleasant tang. Can be eaten hot or cold. (Serves 4–6).

4 oz (100 g) shortcrust pastry
1 large or 2 small cooking apples
3 oz (75 g) melted margarine
3 oz (75 g) wholemeal breadcrumbs
3 oz (75 g) ground almonds
3 oz (75 g) stoned dates
3 tablespoons apple juice
Rind and juice 1 lemon
1 teaspoon nutmeg
1 teaspoon baking powder

## *Method*

Set oven to Gas 5/190°C/375°F.

- Make the pastry and use to line an 8″ (20 cm) pie dish or flan ring. Trim edges.
- Put the dates and apple juice into a pan and simmer for a few minutes until soft. Mash with a fork or liquidize to a smooth purée. Cool slightly.
- Add the margarine, almonds, breadcrumbs, lemon rind and juice, nutmeg and baking powder. Mix well to a stiffish paste.
- Peel and core the apples and chop finely. Fill the base of the prepared pastry case with apple and spread the bakewell mixture on top. Smooth with a knife.
- Bake for 25–30 minutes until the tart is well browned.
- Serve with nutcream, tofu cream or apricot sauce.
- Better if frozen ready cooked and then eaten when thawed.

SWEET
SAUCES

### Nutcream

A thick pouring cream suitable for serving with any hot or cold dessert. It is rich in protein and therefore a good way of improving the nutritive value of a meal. (Serves 4).

    1 oz (25 g) ground cashew nuts
    1 oz (25 g) ground almonds
    1 tablespoon sunflower oil
    2 tablespoons water
    1 teaspoon maple syrup or sugar (optional)

#### *Method*

• Whizz all the ingredients together in a liquidizer until smooth and creamy, adjusting the consistency if desired by adding more water.
• Will keep 2 days refrigerated. Stir before serving.
• Not suitable for freezing.

### Fruity Nutcream

This is a tangy variation on the basic nutcream suitable for serving with any hot or cold dessert. It is a spooning cream but can be made more runny by adjusting the amount of orange juice used. (Serves 4).

    1 oz (25 g) ground cashew nuts

289

1 oz (25 g) ground almonds
1 tablespoon sunflower oil
1 eating apple, peeled, cored and chopped
4 tablespoons orange juice
½ teaspoon ground cardamom

## Method

- Whizz all the ingredients together in a liquidizer until thick and creamy adding more orange juice if desired to make a runny consistency.
- Will keep 2 days refrigerated. Stir before serving.
- Not suitable for freezing.


## Tofu Cream

A lovely pouring cream that is ideal to serve with any sweet, hot or cold. The cream is rich in protein and is a good way of improving the nutritive value of a meal. (To serve 4.)

4 oz (100 g) *silken* tofu
1 dessertspoon maple syrup
1 tablespoon sunflower oil
2 tablespoons apple juice
½ teaspoon vanilla essence

## Method

- Blend all the ingredients together in a liquidizer until smooth and creamy. Add more apple juice if required to achieve a thinner consistency.
- Will keep 2 days refrigerated. Rewhisk before serving.
- Not suitable for freezing.


## Coconut Cream

This rich cream can either be served warm as a pouring sauce or chilled and served as a thick cream. Delicious with crumbles, pies, flans and fruit salads. (Serves 4).

¼ pint (150 ml) boiling water

4 oz (100 g) solid coconut cream (e.g. Sharwoods)
$\frac{1}{4}$ teaspoon ground cardamom

## Method

- Break the coconut cream into small pieces and stir into the boiling water until dissolved.
- Add the cardamom and continue stirring until the cream cools slightly and thickens.
- Serve immediately hot, or chill and serve cold.
- Not suitable for freezing.

## Soya Milk Custard

You could use commercial custard powder to make vegan custard but for those of you who prefer to avoid processed foods that contain additives and colourings, this recipe makes a very delicately flavoured pouring custard suitable for serving hot with sweets or cold with fruit. (Serves 4).

$\frac{1}{2}$ pint (275 ml) soya milk
2 teaspoons vanilla essence
4 rounded teaspoons cornflour
$\frac{1}{4}$ teaspoon nutmeg
1 tablespoon soft brown sugar

## Method

- Mix the cornflour with a little of the soya milk to a smooth paste.
- Put the cornflour paste in a pan with the rest of the soya milk and all the other ingredients. Whisk continuously on a low heat until the custard thickens.
- Serve immediately hot, or cool down then refrigerate and serve cold. Will keep 2 days refrigerated.
- Not suitable for freezing.

*Variation*: *chocolate custard* — to make chocolate custard, whisk 2 oz (50 g) plain vegan chocolate (broken into pieces) into the warm custard until it has melted. Serve immediately. Very popular especially if served with bananas or pears.

## Orange Sauce

A tangy pouring sauce that is delicious hot with sweet pancakes, pies, crumbles and sponge puddings. (To serve 4.)

½ pint (275 ml) orange juice (unsweetened)
Rind 1 orange
1 oz (25 g) margarine
4 rounded teaspoons cornflour
1 dessertspoon soft brown sugar

### Method

• Mix the orange juice and cornflour until smooth. Put into a pan.
• Add all the other ingredients and *whisk* on a low heat until the margarine has melted. Turn heat up and continue whisking until the sauce thickens.
• Serve immediately, warm.
• Freeze in plastic containers and use within 6 weeks. Thin down with a little more orange juice after thawing if necessary.

## Pineapple and Lemon Sauce

Another tangy pouring sauce that is ideal with sponges, crumbles, pancakes and pies. The pineapple pieces give added texture. (Serves 4).

½ pint (275 ml) pineapple juice (unsweetened)
Rind 1 lemon
1 oz (25 g) margarine
4 rounded teaspoons cornflour
1 dessertspoon soft brown sugar
4 oz (100 g) fresh or tinned (unsweetened) pineapple chopped finely
1 teaspoon cinnamon

### Method

• Mix the cornflour with the pineapple juice until smooth. Pour into a pan.
• Add the lemon rind, margarine, sugar and cinnamon. *Whisk* on a low heat until the margarine has melted. Turn the

heat up and continue whisking until the sauce has thickened.

• Stir in the pineapple pieces and serve immediately, warm.

• Freeze in plastic containers and use within 6 weeks. Thin down with a little more pineapple juice after thawing, if necessary.

## Apricot Sauce

A beautiful smooth pouring sauce which is absolutely delicious with pancakes, sponges, bakewell tart and pies. (To serve 4.)

> 2 oz (50 g) dried apricots, finely chopped
> $\frac{1}{4}$ pint (150 ml) orange juice
> Rind $\frac{1}{2}$ orange
> $\frac{1}{2}$ teaspoon mixed spice
> 3 fl oz (75 ml) water

### Method

• Put the apricots in a pan with the orange juice and stew on a low heat for 15 minutes until the fruit is soft. Cool slightly.

• Pour into a liquidizer with the orange rind, spice and water. Whizz until smooth adding more water if necessary to achieve a pouring consistency.

• Return to pan and warm through gently. Serve immediately, warm.

• Freeze in plastic boxes and use within 6 weeks. Add a little more orange juice after thawing if necessary to achieve the desired consistency.

## Chocolate Sauce

This is a rich pouring sauce which is lovely served warm with baked bananas or pears, sponge puddings and flaky pastries such as apple turnovers or cold with fruit salads. (Serves 4).

> 3 oz (75 g) plain vegan chocolate, broken into pieces
> 3 level teaspoons cornflour
> $\frac{1}{2}$ pint (275 ml) water
> 3 oz (75 g) margarine
> 1 tablespoon maple syrup
> $1\frac{1}{2}$ teaspoons vanilla essence

### Method

- Mix the cornflour with some of the cold water to form a paste.
- Put the chocolate in a pan with the rest of the water and stir over a low heat until the chocolate has melted. *Do not boil.*
- Add the cornflour paste, margarine, maple syrup and vanilla. Whisk on a low heat until the margarine has melted and the sauce has thickened.
- Serve immediately warm, or cool and serve cold.
- Not suitable for freezing.

# Recipe Index

# Further Reading

Barkas, J. (1975) *The Vegetable Passion*. Routledge and Kegan Paul, London.

Bender, A.E. (1980) *The Role of Plants in Feeding Mankind*. The Vegan Society, Oxford.

Benjamin, H. (1974) *Commonsense Vegetarianism*. Thorsons Publishers, Northants.

Brown, S. (1985) *Healthy Living Cookbook*, Dorling Kindersley, London.

Commission For Racial Equality (1982). *A Guide to Asian Diets*.

Dent, J. (1982) Teaching Children the Vegetarian Ideal. *The Vegetarian*, Sept/Oct.

DHSS. (1981) *Rickets and Osteomalacia*. HMSO.

Dickerson, J.W.T. (1979) *Plant Foods for Human Health*. The Vegan Society, Oxford.

Dickerson, J.W.T. and Ellis, F.R. (1977) Vegetarianism — a clinician's view. *Nutrition and Food Science*, 48, pp. 6–8.

Elliott, R. (1984) *Vegetarian Mother and Baby Book*. Fontana, London.

Hills, L.D. (1974) *The Comfrey Report*. Henry Doubleday Research Association.

HMSO (1976) *Manual of Nutrition*. Ministry of Agriculture, Fisheries and Food

Jannaway, K. (1985) *Sustaining and Sustainable*. The Movement for Compassionate Living, Dec. issue.

Jannaway, K. (1985) *Making the Most of World Resources*. The Movement for Compassionate Living, Aug issue.

Jeans, H. (1973) *Natural Oils from Nuts and Seeds*. Thorsons Publishers, Northants.

Long, A. (1981) The Well Nourished Vegetarian. *New Scientist*, pp. 330–33.

Long, A. (1982) Meat and Milk the Foods that Cry. *The Vegetarian*, July/Aug.

Long, A. (1982) The World Food Problem — The Facts of Life. *The Vegetarian*, Sept/Oct.

Lucas, J.W. (1979) *Vegetarian Nutrition*. The Vegetarian Society, London.

Mindell, E. (1979) *The Vitamin Bible*. Arlington Books Ltd. London.

Moore-Lappe, F. (1975) *Diet for a Small Planet*. Ballantine Books.

Moran, V. (1985) *Compassion, the Ultimate Ethic*. Thorsons Publishers, Northants.

Polunin, M. (1979) *Minerals* Thorsons, Publishers, Northants.

Purves, R. (1981) Vegan Diets for Young Children *Nutrition and Food Science* 68, pp. 4–6

Robertson, I. *et al.* (1982) Nutritional Deficiencies among Ethnic Minorities in the United Kingdom. *Proceedings of the Nutrition Society*, 41, 2, pp. 243–55.

Sanders, T.A.B. and Ellis, F.R. (1981) *Vegan Nutrition*. The Vegan Society, Oxford.

Shurtleff, W. and Aoyagi, A. (1976) *The Book of Miso* Autumn Press.

Vegan Society, *Is Cow Milk Good For You?* (leaflet).

Vegan Society, *Living the Vegan Way* (leaflet).

Vegan Society, *The Honey Question* (leaflet)

Vegan Society, *The Reasons for Veganism* (leaflet)

Vegan Society, *Vegan Mothers and Children* (leaflet)

Vegan Society, *Two Population Explosions* (leaflet).

Vegan Society, *Wool Machines* (leaflet).

Vegan Society, *Whatever Happens to the Calf?* (leaflet).

Vegan Society, *What Happens To The Kid?* (leaflet).

Vegetarian Society, *Infant Feeding* (leaflet).

Vegetarian Society, *Three Myths — the vegetarian answer* (leaflet).

Vegetarian Society, *The World Food Problem* (leaflet).

Wynne-Tyson, J. (1976) *Food For A Future*, Centaur Press, Sussex.

Yntema, S. (1980) *The Vegetarian Baby*. Thorsons Publishers Ltd., Northants.

# Useful Addresses

*Animal Aid*
7 Castle Street, Tonbridge, Kent. TN9 1BH.

*Beauty Without Cruelty Ltd*
Avebury Avenue, Tonbridge, Kent. TN9 1TL.

*Body Shop, The* (Cruelty-free cosmetics)
Hawthorne Road, Wick, Littlehampton, W. Sussex. BN17 7LR.

*Bright Eyes Cosmetics*
56 Bell Street, Glasgow. G1 1LQ.

*British Union for the Abolition of Vivisection (BUAV)*
16a Crane Grove, Islington, London. N7 8LB.

*Chicken's Lib*
6 Pilling Lane, Skelmanthorpe, Huddersfield.

*Compassion in World Farming*
20 Lavant Street, Petersfield, Hampshire. GU32 3EW

*Dr. Hadwen Trust for Humane Research*
Tylers Way, Watford, Herts. WD2 8HQ

*Faith Products Ltd.* (Cruelty-free cosmetics)
52/56 Albion Road, Edinburgh. EH7 5QZ.

*Free Range Egg Association*
39 Maresfield Gardens, London. NW3 5SG.

*Friends of the Earth*
377 City Road, London. EC1V 1NA.

*Greenpeace*
36 Graham Street, London. W1 2JX.

*League Against Cruel Sports*
83–87 Union Street, London. SE1 1SG.

*Lynx* (Anti-fur organisation)
PO Box 509, Dunmow, Essex. CM6 1UH.

*Movement for Compassionate Living* (The Vegan Way)
47 Highlands Road, Leatherhead, Surrey. KT22 8NQ.

*RSPCA*
Causeway, Horsham, West Sussex. RH12 1HG.

*Tiki Cosmetics*
Sisson Road, Gloucester. GL1 3QB.

*Vegan Society*
33–35 George Street, Oxford. OX1 2AY.

*Vegan Views* (a quarterly magazine for vegan opinion)
c/o H. Mather, 6 Hayes Avenue, Bournemouth. BH7 7AD.

*Vegetarian Society*
Parkdale, Dunham Road, Altrincham, Cheshire. WA14 4QG.

*Weleda (UK) Ltd.* (Cruelty-free cosmetics)
Heanor Road, Ilkeston, Derbyshire DE7 8DR.